STO ✓

CHESTNUT CUB

CHESTNUT CUB

by

B. F. BEEBE

Illustrated by

JAMES RALPH JOHNSON

DAVID McKAY COMPANY, INC.

New York

1963

CHESTNUT CUB

For
Beulah Beebe
Cherryvale, Kansas

1: Outside World

THE MOUNTAIN LIONS WANTED TO ATTACK THE FEMALE BEAR the morning her cubs were born. This happened when the lion pair, or "painters" to the older settlers here in North Carolina's Great Smokies, paused before a snowbank on the north slope of Twentymile Ridge.

They pushed their nostrils into the air vent leading into the bear's den, and spread ears forward to hear the muffled whimpers. The scent and sound lifted their hackles and their tails twisted in anger, a movement which caused an overhead squirrel to bark sharp warnings that were repeated by his kin across the ravine.

The snowbank was a distasteful obstacle, however. The instinctive enmity between mountain lion and bear was as bitter as that between dog and cat, but instinct also told the lion pair to await a better time. They did not have many moments to waste before climbing back up the ridge to their own den where the heavy female would give birth to her own cubs.

The mother bear had no awareness of the inquisitive lions. Her thoughts were fully occupied this late January morning. The two cubs were her first. It had taken over three years' growth for her to reach maturity, and now all her senses were attuned to caring for these mewling young ones.

Both were smaller than chipmunks, neither weighing over ten ounces. A porcupine's baby was actually larger at birth than a black bear cub, for there were few examples in the animal world of such disparity in the weights of mother and offspring. The mother bear weighed over two hundred times as much as either cub.

She licked the naked young ones dry and nosed them against the two mammary glands between her rear legs. The four milk glands on her chest would not be used by the cubs until the family left the den, but here her rear legs provided added protection for the helpless newborn whose eyelids were closed tight.

The mother bear had hibernated in early December. Although there were some American areas of mild climates where black bears did not bother to hibernate, these North Carolina mountain slopes had Canada's climate, and the bear population went underground before the heavy snows came.

In contrast to the natural tie which permanently bound the lion pair, she had no use for her brief mate of over seven months ago. He led a solitary life throughout the year except for a week or so in early summer, as did she.

Surprisingly, the mother bear was not in the state of half-stupor which characterized bears without cubs during hibernation. When she had first entered this den she had curled

up and fallen into natural sleep, but she was easily awakened, and any snap of a twig outside brought her to her feet.

After a few days, however, her sleep deepened, and breathing and blood circulation slowed while her fat gradually degenerated. Carbon waste remained in her blood stream since normal body functions did not throw it off, and this carbonic-acid gas tended to dull her conscious senses, but not her motherhood instincts.

She slept most of each day now, but her senses remained receptive to the needs of the cubs. They whimpered whenever they were hungry—even as early as an hour after birth—and she nudged them to a feeding spot when they had trouble finding one.

Their eyes stayed closed for the first forty days. This was no inconvenience since there was nothing to do but eat and sleep, and the cubs grew quickly. By February the snowbank began melting and the den's interior gradually grew lighter.

If the mother bear noticed a difference in her two cubs now she gave no indication of it, for both were tended with the same gentle care. They were different, however.

When they were first born only a suggestion of hair was to be found on them, but now rich black hair coated one cub to give it the same appearance as any other Smoky Mountain bear cub. There was considerable difference in the other's appearance. He was as brown as a chestnut and a splash of white hair on his chest made a rumpled pattern across it.

"Little Chestnut" would have been common in Yellowstone and other parts of the Rocky Mountains where up to half of the black bears wore coats of brown, rust or chestnut. Here in the East, however, a chestnut cub was virtually unknown.

Unfortunately for Little Chestnut, when the den grew light enough for the mother bear to distinguish her cubs' colors, she was not particularly attracted to his brown coat. Bears are as individual in some of their traits as human beings, and what pleases one bear might irritate another.

In early March she pushed her nose through the snowbank at the point where the sun made its brightest sparkles, and led her cubs from the den. From that time Little Chestnut's troubles began. The first moments outside were awesome in contrast to the snug den. The mother bear ambled along lapping snow every few steps. She was not hungry now as might be expected since her stomach had shriveled from disuse during hibernation.

Little Chestnut followed close behind his brother cub, floundering through the soft snow from one huge footprint to another. To the cubs these were pitfalls in the snow, and they struggled out of each with much effort.

The mother bear walked ahead for a few yards before stopping periodically to look back at her cubs' predicament. Then she moved back on shuffling feet which plowed a pathway for them, and nosed them up from the pitfalls. Then they struggled after her for a few more feet before the action was repeated, again and again.

Finally they reached a sunny southern slope where the ground was threaded with sparkling rivulets of melting snow. She dipped her nose into this icy water and lapped eagerly to satisfy a consuming thirst which had built over the past weeks.

Little Chestnut shared none of her pleasure, however. His feet sank into the spongy leaf layer over which this water trickled, and almost every step meant a surge of chilling water halfway up his leg.

He stopped on each stone of any size to lift each foot and try to fling the water from it. The larger black cub appeared to be little bothered by the cold water because he could leap over most rivulets and stay close on his mother's heels.

After a few moments of this, Little Chestnut looked up to see the mother bear almost out of sight in the laurel bushes ahead, and he gave a plaintive wail like that of a lonesome puppy. The mother turned and grunted a sharp warning for him to join her, but when he stepped off his rock both front feet sank into springy moss so far that he had to rear back to prevent his nose going under.

This situation was reason enough to Little Chestnut for remaining on the rock, but it was not for his mother. She came trotting back and slapped him off the rock, skidding him several feet through ice water. When he climbed to his feet he was soaked, but he wasted no time splashing after her when she turned downslope again.

She did not go many yards before turning aside to a natural nest of dry leaves which the wind had gathered among tree roots. Here she settled to her haunches and leaned back against the tree before opening her forelegs and grunting softly to summon the cubs.

Little Chestnut scampered forward and leaped into her lap a bound ahead of his brother. There for the next hour the mother bear combed their fur dry with her tongue while they pressed against her warm chest and nursed. Finally both fell asleep with the sun on their faces.

At dusk the mother bear rolled them over into the leaves to awaken them for further travel. They did not go far this time, however. After she drank from the stream below the laurels she led them into thick brush and curled around them for the night.

This was the schedule over the next few days. The family would not return to the den again. If the cubs were still with her next winter she might take them to the same den, but the chances were that she would find a new one by then.

Her movement was consistently downslope now, and Little Chestnut tagged along behind his brother as they worked down rugged ravines. Each stop was in air warmer than the last, and by the end of the second day they were in dense brush fully leafed and thick with buds which the mother bear nibbled occasionally.

These first days outside the den were casual ones for the mother bear as her appetite slowly built toward normal. The cubs had none of her sluggishness, however, and Little Chestnut was ever exploring. Even while he nursed, his eyes studied the sights around him.

Mist and haze made distant peaks look soft like clouds. These were the sights the frontiersmen had seen when they named these mountains "The Great Smokies." These heavily forested mountains had no counterpart. They had arrested time from centuries past and preserved it, the virgin forests on these Smoky Mountain peaks and in its steep canyons forming the largest remaining primeval forest in the East.

These first weeks of exploration were a time of constant fascination to Little Chestnut. He grew quickly but his weight never caught up with the black cub's. His claws were as sharp, though, and whenever he clutched too hard at his mother's chest she grunted sharply. If this did not stop the claws she brushed him out onto the ground.

It was rough treatment but not especially unkind, because nature had built ample protection into the bear-cub bodies. Skins were thick, muscles were powerful, and bones were strong.

The mother's milk grew less vital each day. Since bears are omnivorous animals—eating both plant and animal life— Little Chestnut sampled everything that he could slap flat or gnaw.

Play occupied the two cubs almost every minute not spent

in eating or sleeping. The mother bear looked on their incessant romping and wrestling with tolerance since it developed their bodies and skills, but when she tried to nap and they used her for a wrestling mat, she soon put a stop to it.

Such rebuffs seldom dampened Little Chestnut's exuberance. There was always some suitable playmate—a stick, butterfly, or grass clump—beyond the next rock. Sometimes there was another young animal, or even a bird. However, his first encounter with young birds made him view with caution any future temptations to join them for a romp.

After a half hour of play on his mother's soft back one June afternoon Little Chestnut was finally stopped by her growl. He hesitated only a moment before quietly nosing off into the weeds behind her, and she apparently thought he settled against her flank alongside the black cub because she gave no warning grunt.

After a few yards Little Chestnut climbed over a natural fence of rock outcropping which bordered a woodland clearing. On the other side he moved into the shadows of yard-high umbrella leaves, native plants which looked like ragged elephant-ear plants of the tropics. His ears remained alert in case his mother growled, so he made no noise.

Shortly he stepped into the sunlight, then stopped when he became aware of movement about him. It took a long look around to identify what caused it.

The movement was made by wild-turkey poults, or chicks, already several weeks away from their early May hatching. Their curiosity was no less keen than Little Chestnut's, and the half-feathered young turkeys were absorbed in busy explorations under every leaf and bark piece.

Little Chestnut's interest perked up immediately at the prospect of chasing these energetic young birds. But he had time only to gather muscles for a leap when he heard a sharp "purt!"

The sound came from a turkey hen beyond the poults, and in the next moment several things happened. The poults simply melted from sight as if the leaf layer had absorbed them. The turkey hen jumped into the air and flapped heavily to a lower limb beyond the clearing, as did several other hens.

Of more consequence was Little Chestnut's abrupt introduction to a grown tom turkey, a bird both jealous and intolerant of intruders. With wings flailing, the crotchety old bird came at Little Chestnut like a monstrous hornet. His feet swept forward and Little Chestnut had only a glimpse of curving spurs behind each leg.

The turkey managed to get in only one good lick, a stiff peck with his thorny beak, before Little Chestnut whirled in retreat. It caught Little Chestnut on one hip and sent him squealing through the weed stalks. He did not slow until he was over the rocks again, and in sight of the mother bear whose alerted movement caught the black cub like a cushion beneath her.

Little Chestnut heard his brother cub's surprised squeal, but it was slight compared to the triumphant "obble-obble!" from beyond the rocks. Then he heard his mother's displeased growl. It was sufficient to tell him that this would be his last such excursion.

Although many animals could be judged by the traits of the species, such general estimates were of little use in identifying traits of the two cubs as they grew rapidly over the next weeks. They were as different in temperament as any two boys of the same family.

Because the black cub was larger and stronger he soon fell into a habit of allowing Little Chestnut to find a morsel among the rocks, then taking it away from him in a short furious fight. This was unfortunate for the black cub since it retarded skills necessary for food-getting, while it stimulated them in Little Chestnut.

Perhaps it was a natural situation, too, for the mother to allow occasional favors to the black cub which were denied Little Chestnut. The black cub was a reflection of herself in appearance while Little Chestnut was not. As a consequence, the black cub was allowed the favored spot next to her stomach when the family curled up for the night. Little Chestnut had to find his spot elsewhere.

The black cub was often allowed first choice when she lifted a rock slab to expose insect larva, and Little Chestnut soon learned that the most satisfactory thing for him to do was to pull over his own rocks. This growing self-reliance was to be invaluable to Little Chestnut. It soon saved him from a painful experience which left the black cub bawling and helpless.

2: *Honey-coated Trouble*

THE MOTHER BEAR CRAVED HONEY ABOVE ALL WILDERNESS FOODS. When she spotted bees entering and leaving a cracked blackgum tree one June afternoon, she immediately sent the cubs into the mountain laurel along a mountain stream to wait while she climbed the tree.

The trunk was well decayed and when she reached the crack she had no trouble ripping off sufficient splinters to allow her forepaws to reach inside this wild-bee hive.

This was laurel honey which was poisonous to some human beings and animal life. Beemasters on the valley farms cleaned honey from their hives as soon as the laurel quit blooming so the bees would refill the hives with sourwood honey, the best in the mountains.

But the bears had no such concerns. All honey was acceptable. The mother bear pushed a foot inside the trunk and lifted out a section of dripping honeycomb. She stuffed this into her mouth while holding herself against the tree with her other feet.

With the honeycomb, however, came a swarm of furious bees. The roar they made was enough to send the black cub shrinking farther into the laurels, but Little Chestnut watched in fascination as the insects swarmed about his mother's face.

Her squalls contained both pain and rage, but since the honey taste far outweighed the hurts, she continued dipping her paw into the stickiness to dish out wads of dripping comb. Periodically she varied the procedure to wipe off bees from her face, a messy procedure at best since it left facial hair matted with honey and bees caught in their own gluelike product.

Only when the forepaw brought out more woody debris than honey did she slow her feeding. She backed slowly down the trunk like a heavily laden lineman descending a telephone pole, and still bawling occasionally as stinging bees made her miserable.

The black cub waited only until her rear feet touched the ground before scrambling forward toward her, his fright heightened by the noise she made, and under the impression that safety lay as close to the mother bear as he could get.

Little Chestnut, however, had reservations. He could see the bees, and he could hear their anger. Rising on hind feet he waited until the situation became clear, or the mother bear called.

Before the mother bear dropped to all four feet, the black cub leaped for her back. His sharp claws dug through her hair to secure a firm anchor in her thick skin.

During the next moment Little Chestnut watched the bees turn their attention on this new target while the mother bear shook herself to get rid of her scratching rider. The black cub squealed like a frightened young pig as bee stingers found their marks in his thinner skin, and he clutched his mother all the harder.

Protective instincts overruled those of motherhood during the next moment as the mother bear rushed through laurel and rhododendron bushes lining the stream behind Little Chestnut. He saw the black cub knocked from her back as she swept under a log. She did not slow but plunged from a high bank to hit the water spread-eagled, splashing it out on both banks. She hugged the bottom for a moment before surfacing.

The squealing black cub's troubles were not finished. He scampered to the bank where he stopped to slap at the bees. For each one hit several more stung him. Then the mother bear reached up and slapped him into the stream.

Only a half dozen bees found the quietly watching Little Chestnut as his mother and brother cub soothed their pains in the cold water. Little Chestnut slapped each bee flat before stingers could be used, and ate them with considerable enjoyment since the melee had caused them to be coated with honey. By the end of a half hour when the bedraggled mother and black cub sloshed from the water, there were no bees in sight.

The mountain streams became well known to Little Chestnut over succeeding days. The cool shadows beneath streambank vegetation allowed comfortable explorations and naps on hot days. The warm June sun opened the rhododendron buds into huge red blossoms and these were soon followed by white balls of mountain laurel blossoms. The petals of both flowers dropped steadily into the streams to add their hues to waters already colored a warm brown by leaves. These waters had varying acid contents because of these droppings and the results dictated which fish would live in them.

Because fish were much sought after by the mother bear she explored the streams daily. These stream beds were ideal for bear travels anyway since they were an endless series of rock shelves. Deep pools were contained between expanses of white water.

At highest elevations these pools were filled with native brook trout. The mother bear stalked these fish by wading slowly upstream, then settling to her haunches in a likely spot where she remained motionless. The brook trout had the keenest vision and were the wariest of the three trout here in the Smokies. The slightest movement sent them flying like sun rays breaking past scudding clouds.

The trout depended upon sight for detection of danger as well as for food-getting, and the optic lobes of their brains were large in comparison to the brains of catfish and suckers whose olfactory lobes were larger in proportion. The latter fish were more dependent upon the sense of smell for food-getting.

Most people assumed bears flipped fish out onto the banks,

but this was rarely, if ever, done. Water compressed but little between bear paw and fish side, and an alert fish had little trouble avoiding a bear swipe. A bear paw slammed down from the rear, however, was not apt to be detected until too late.

The mother bear sat still until a trout drifted within reach. Then a powerful forepaw moved quickly to pin the trout against the bottom, and she dipped her head underwater to seize it.

Since many fish parasites lived best in hard alkaline water, the brook trout avoided these waters and congregated in the mountain pools of softer, more acid, water. This was important to these trout since their tiny scales allowed easier access to parasites than the large scales of rainbow and brown trout.

The brook trout were easier to find in daylight since they fed more during the day than their kin of lower streams. Although their colors changed in a few moments' time to mimic the bottom coloration, the mother bear had learned what to watch for. When the fish hovered above a dark bottom their red-and-white ventral and pectoral, or bottom, fins showed distinctively.

Oddly, brook trout flesh varied in color according to the food eaten. If there were many fresh-water shrimps and mayfly nymphs available the flesh was red. If the brook trout fed on the tiny aquatic life in the bottom gravel the flesh was pink.

The two other mountain trout here, the rainbows and

browns, were not natives like the brook. The browns had been introduced from Europe in the 1930's and could thrive in water too warm for the brook trout. This was fine since so many trees had been cut from mountain streambanks that the sunlight often made former brook trout waters too warm for the brooks.

The browns made themselves at home in the quiet water behind beaver dams, and did little feeding before sunset. The rainbows had many of these traits also, and both thrived even in the lakes into which mountain streams emptied.

There was one fishing technique which pleased Little Chestnut considerably. Occasionally the mother bear would station the two cubs by a pool while she climbed above it. Then she rolled boulders into the water. Frightened fish sometimes leaped out onto the banks and Little Chestnut pounced happily upon those within reach.

Invariably, however, the black cub found that the easiest way to capture a fish was to take it from his brother. Little Chestnut raised no great objection to this procedure at first, but after a few repetitions he dropped his fish and piled into the bullying brother with flashing claws and teeth. If this did not slow the aggression and fighting continued, the mother came scrambling down to cuff the two apart, and as often as not most of the prize fish went to the black cub anyway.

Growth was rapid in both cubs during these summer months and the mother led them on ever-expanding trips.

There was much for a cub to learn about wildlife in these mountains because there was so much variety in the animal life here. More than fifty fur-bearing animals lived in these mountains, as well as two hundred bird species, eighty reptiles and amphibians, eighty fishes, and uncounted insects.

It seemed that each slope and mountainside visited was a little different from the others. Some of these slopes were little visited except by bears, while others had to be shared with most wildlife species. Little Chestnut loved to explore the grass and heath balds which few other animals used now except the bears.

There was argument among the mountain men about how the grass balds began, but the best guess seemed to be that they had been cleared first by Cherokee Indians and early settlers for stock grazing and had never reforested naturally.

The Indians had a handy method of clearing such mountain land. They never wasted time and energy hacking down trees with their crude axes. Instead they girdled the trees in an area selected for clearing by smashing a belt of bark off the trunk. This cut all the sap lines and the tree wilted and died within days. The naked trees were left standing for several seasons as crops of corn, pumpkin and squash were grown in the sunlit ground. When the trunks were completely dry they were sometimes set afire, although the most popular method was to ignore them until a windstorm brought them down.

The Indians who escaped the forced removal of Cherokees

to Oklahoma in the 1830's used the grass balds both for stock grazing and farming since these cloud-strewn sites were nearly inaccessible. White settlers of the late 1800's kept the grass balds bare by herding sheep and cattle on them during the cool summers.

On lower slopes were heath balds, or "laurel slicks," which were deceiving as to their true character. From a short distance away the carpet of rhododendron, cherry birch and mountain laurel looked soft and smooth. However, Little Chestnut never saw any indication of human visits in them. Any man who tried to walk across one found that the intertwined limbs reaching past his head made an impenetrable barrier. The only route through a laurel slick was along a bear, or wild boar tunnel and no man in his right mind would attempt to crawl into one of these.

The laurel slicks had been caused by natural disasters—land slides and fires—which destroyed the forest and opened the slopes to laurels and birches. Eventually such slicks would give way to shading forest giants which waded slowly in from the edges.

It would have been well if the mother bear had spent more time in these balds which were so uninviting to most other wildlife, especially to the fastidious mountain lions who stayed clear of these dripping bushes.

3: Unseen Clue

It was an early July morning when the mother bear passed the lion marker by less than ten feet. That she did not notice it was unusual since black bears depended on smell and hearing, rather than sight, to detect danger. The lion marker was full of fresh scent.

The lion marker was nothing but two eight-inch scrapes in the leaf layer made by a mountain lion's feet less than a half hour before. Such scrapes pointed out the direction taken to other lions, and served as a notice against trespassing to other large animals which might contest hunting rights.

Several things prevented the mother bear from detecting the lion scent, however. At dawn she and her cubs had crossed back into the Qualla Tract of the Cherokee Indian Reservation. It was a sanctuary to her like the Smoky Mountain National Park and there was no likelihood of an angry farmer taking a shot at them. Nor would there be a possibility of trail dogs running loose here on Lickstone Ridge which was nearly a mile above sea level. She could hear puppies playing in a Cherokee farmyard down in Soco Creek Valley, but there was nothing to suggest a hazard up here on these shadowed slopes.

Unfortunately she fed downwind as she turned over stones in her search for insects and grubs. Little Chestnut mimicked her actions in lifting stones and flipping them to either side instead of toward himself as a human being would do. Bear legs were powerful, the most powerful of any Smoky Mountain animal, and he easily managed to displace stone slabs as big as pie plates. He slapped scurrying insects against the ground to stop them, then dabbed them up with his tongue.

Both cubs were too full of energy to search for long. Every few steps Little Chestnut stopped to box his brother's hind quarters, or fend off the latter's slap. Such action invariably started a wrestling bout and the two kept it up for several moments until the mother bear put a stop to it by growling. If they were so busy playing that they paid no attention to this growling she cuffed them apart.

This roughness disturbed the cubs very little. Their tough young bodies were already networks of hard muscles and they resumed their food-getting until another opportunity for wrestling presented itself.

This was not long in coming. They were still a hundred yards upwind of the lion marker when they saw the hemlock log across their route. There was a scramble up its rotten sides as each cub tried to gain the top first in order to push the other back.

They both arrived at the same time and squared off like

boxers for a new bout. Both reared on hind feet and began a slapping contest. The mother bear looked up from her feeding and decided they could not get into trouble for the moment, so she resumed her search under the rocks.

She was wrong. The cubs wrestled down the log's length, their young claws digging out soft wood chips as they struggled for balance. They had no inkling of movement inside the log below them.

There was a skunk there, exploring for insect grubs as did the bears, and the commotion above him suggested some nuisance threatening his own food hunt. He walked out the log's open end.

Little Chestnut scampered down the log now with the black cub in close pursuit. Sensing the black cub behind him he stopped near the end and whirled about. As his snout probed for his brother's neck the latter lifted his head aside and brought up a forepaw in retaliation.

The blow caught Little Chestnut on the shoulder with enough force to spoil his footing and his hind legs slid down either side of the log before he stopped astride it.

Cub jaws nipped at every available target as claws dug into the bark. Little Chestnut's claws shortly dug into dead bark which slid away in a slab, and he followed it down head first, urged on by a slap of his upturned rear which the black cub managed just in time. The latter leaped off in pursuit.

The mother bear did not see them momentarily when they

spotted the skunk. They stopped their game abruptly and headed for this new playmate. Each cub, alone, would have had an instinctive caution about approaching the white-striped animal, but the enthusiasm of competition had possession of them now. Each was determined that the other would not arrive first.

The skunk did not hesitate when he saw this approaching scramble of cubs. He threw his hindquarters to one side. They were still ten feet away when a squirt of liquid shot from underneath his lifted tail.

The liquid was no different in appearance from yellow water sprayed from a water pistol, but its repulsive odor was something which had no match in the American wilderness. The scientist termed it *n-Butyl Mercaptan,* and it was powerful enough to cause permanent blindness when an adequate dose hit an animal in the eyes. More than one skunked trail hound, too far from its master to receive prompt first aid, had lost its vision because of this poisonous spray.

However, instinct turned the cubs in time for them to receive the spray only along their sides. Squealing in sudden panic, they both raced toward their mother now standing on hind legs, with head held high in an effort to see what was taking place.

She was not prepared for the mad scramble. She had started to lean forward to all fours in an effort to dodge her ill-smelling young ones when they struck her lap, each trying to outdo the other in getting to this place of refuge first.

The surprised mother bear had little sympathy for her miserable young ones. She propelled them from her lap as if they were hot coals thrown from a burning log, then turned to gallop along the ridge in full flight.

This did not discourage the cubs in the least. They stayed at her heels as she headed for a stream splashing toward Soco Creek. It was then that she passed the lion marker without sensing its presence, a situation which would not have happened except for the overpowering skunk odor.

Under normal conditions her nose would have caught this deliberately placed mountain lion scent immediately and turned her in the opposite direction since the mountain lion was the only Smoky Mountain animal which offered a real hazard to a black bear in a fight. An instinctive hatred of unsuspected intensity existed between the two species. To the casual animal observer such behavior seemed uncharacteristic of the secretive mountain lion. Even the oldest mountain people had seldom seen one in the wild, so furtive were its movements. Yet the mountain lion often went out of its way to attack the slower-moving bear, and did so with confidence. The lion was usually victorious.

When the mother bear reached a pothole below a waterfall she leaped from the bank without slowing and hit the water with spread legs. This action was startling to the trout there and they flashed in all directions, several spurting out onto a pebble flat.

The bear had no interest in them now, however. She twisted and rolled in the chilling water, scrubbing herself against the bottom gravel in an effort to rub off the skunk odor. Her cubs were treading anxiously on the bank when she surfaced, and before she had time to shake the water from her eyes they leaped for her head where their busy feet attempted to find firm footing along her face.

Snorting angrily, she ducked underwater and shoved past them to the pool's edge. She lifted herself free and turned to face the two struggling cubs. As they pulled themselves out she cuffed them back, again and again. Finally they lost enthusiasm for continuing their futile efforts to get atop her, and waded along the shallows and out onto the gravel bank. Here they sat down wearily and shook water from their fur.

With this forced washing finished the mother bear turned into the woodland to shove herself along the leaves in an attempt to scrape away more skunk odor. Her soft growl told her bedraggled young ones to follow her example, and they climbed along behind, shoving themselves into the moist dirt exposed by her movement.

A half hour passed before the mother bear allowed them to approach close again, and this only after she had led them into the cold stream again. Now she licked their faces dry as they stood on hind legs before her head to seek her attentions and bury their faces in her fur.

She had no clue to the fact that the mountain lion mother

and her two cubs were less than two hundred yards above her on the ridgecrest. The skunk smell which obliterated all other smells from bear nostrils at the moment also hid the bear scent from the mountain lion family.

The lion cubs were sleeping on the sunny leaves before their mother and the male lion had settled to his stomach atop a boulder fifty yards away where he could detect any hazard to his family. He was an omnipresent guardian—like the dog fox, or the father coyote—and although he seldom came close enough to play with the lion cubs, he was always close enough to rush to their aid if danger threatened.

The mother bear soon had her fill of trying to lick clean her smelly cubs. Although they had nearly been weaned, they still made pests of themselves every chance they got since it was much easier to enjoy an easy meal of milk than to search an hour for insects. They began jumping for the mammary glands on her chest. She cuffed them away, but after the skunk incident and wild chase they were anxious to stay as close to their mother as possible.

She broke into a run uphill. It would be better to exhaust the cubs than to try wearing them down by boxing them away. They scrambled after her again, both squealing their desperate little cries.

The noise brought the male lion to his feet, and in another moment he saw the bear heading directly for his mate and her cubs. He leaped to the ground.

The bear had no knowledge of the lion family's presence until she saw the two lions leap into sight like the surge of a mountain stream over a hidden rock. They were two bounds away before she could stop and then it was too late.

4: Night of Fear

THE TWO CUBS SCRAMBLED FOR THE NEAREST TREE, A TOWERING slender-boled tulip poplar whose foliage formed part of the highest canopy overhead. The mother bear waited only until her cubs were safely climbing before trying to climb the tree herself. She never made it.

The furious male lion stretched out in a long leap to land atop the bear. One front foot reached for the bear's throat while his teeth pushed into her neck. The thick muscles there saved her momentarily, and she threw herself to the ground in a violent roll.

This dislodged the lion, but now the mother lion was at the bear's side, her claws digging at the black hair.

The bear cubs waited nervously in a limb fork forty feet up and watched the vicious fighting below. There was no place for the mother bear to turn without meeting lion claws and teeth. When she twisted to defend against one attacker the other lion struck. Finally she managed to drag herself up the poplar trunk with the lion pair still tearing at her. When they could no longer find footholds they slid back to the ground.

The lions circled the tree for the next few moments to assure themselves that the bear offered no further threat.

Then they padded away on stiff legs, pausing every few steps to make certain that the bears stayed up the tree.

From his high perch Little Chestnut saw the lion cubs trot from the bushes when the mother lion squalled. They fell in at her heels as she moved rapidly along the mountain slope with the male lion ranging upslope to one side. In another moment the mountain lions were out of sight, headed for the mountains to the west which seemed to melt into a smoky horizon. The moisture in the air caused this distant haze, and nourished these luxuriant forests which concealed the four-mile-thick rock layer out of which the mountains were carved.

After a few moments Little Chestnut watched the mother bear back awkwardly down the trunk. Her claws seemed to slip each time she placed them on the bark, and she fell the last four feet. The hair at her back was matted and red. She rested a moment before wrestling herself back against the tree trunk where she sat on her haunches as she had done often when nursing the cubs.

The mother bear gave no grunt to tell the cubs to come down but Little Chestnut sensed that she would not rebuff him this time. He began backing down, and the black cub followed him. He slid to the ground beside her and glanced at her face to check the wisdom of climbing into her lap.

The mother bear's face was impassive, however. She seemed half asleep and disinterested in what took place. He climbed cautiously into her lap and pushed an exploratory

[37]

nose against her chest. She made no move to stop him, nor the black cub climbing up from the other side.

Instead, she slipped a foreleg under each, more carefully this time than she commonly did, and slid the cubs up until they found nursing places. While they nursed she licked their faces, her rough tongue combing their fur smooth. It seemed now that she sensed an urgency. The time for schooling her cubs was suddenly gone. There was only time to comfort her young and to do this quickly. She was incapable of thinking about future events or of reasoning in the way human beings did, but instinct had stepped in to whisper that she had joined the parade of fading life.

The cubs' teeth were sharp, but there was no pain at her chest. Her forelegs drew her cubs even closer as her methodical tongue labored, and her administrations gradually slowed.

As the afternoon grew hot and dry Little Chestnut lolled contentedly in the mother bear's firm support. He had no reason to pay any attention to the clouds building on the southern horizon, nor to the distant rumble of thunder. Before long the breeze picked up and Little Chestnut stopped his meal long enough to hold up his nose and feel the wind which blew away the gnats before his nostrils. The black cub decided it was missing something and followed his example.

There was a stretch of quiet water in the stream below which was well grown with golden club plants whose narrow leaves floated like those of the water lily. Their fruiting spires were curved like thin duck heads lifted high, and the breeze seemingly made them rear nervously as if to look for a suspected intruder.

The mountain laurels overhanging the stream shed their faded petals before the breeze like summer snow, and the current built drifts of these petals in the eddies. As the wind built, orange clumps of angel's trumpet blossoms swung erratically on their vine supports as if seeking shelter. The thunderheads were closer now, and Little Chestnut saw occasional outbreaks of lightning filling the sky between clouds and mountain slopes.

The atmosphere's low pressure allowed distant smells and sounds to reach him. He could even smell the gas bubbles rising from valley bogs, the gas formed by decomposing leaves and other vegetable matter on stream bottoms. Lower pressure allowed the bubbles to burst free of the mud and rise to the surface. At night many such bubbles were ignited by spontaneous combustion and the eerie balls of illumination were called will-o'-the-wisps by the mountain people.

Shortly the curtain of rain dragging below the clouds faded the opposite slope from view and the leaves overhead suddenly shuddered under rain drops. The rain was cold and Little Chestnut pushed close to the mother bear's body. It seemed cold, however, and more rigid than it had been. He was soaked by the time the rain moved on to the north. The movement was so gradual that he was unprepared for the next event.

A white-oak tree near by burst in a flash of light and cracking splinters. Lightning had struck the tree to boil and expand sap so quickly that the pressures blew out wood splinters like the explosion of a falling stone shattering beneath a high cliff.

One splinter, as long as the mother bear's body, was hurled into the ground only inches away where it vibrated like a limber spear shaft for the next moment. She made no instinctive movement to dodge, however. Her head no longer moved, and Little Chestnut saw that her eyes reflected the mist of distant mountains. She was dead.

Little Chestnut made no noise for a time. He was puzzled by this change in his mother. He tried to get a reaction from her by cautiously slapping her nose as he had done in play. But even this failed to disturb her.

Her body heat was gone completely by nightfall and she was as immovable as the tree trunk behind her. He began to whimper his impatience, a tactic the black cub quickly copied.

Although black bears could be as quiet as shadows they could also make numerous sounds. The mother bear had often growled threateningly like other animals, or coughed sharply to warn of danger. When the cubs were hurt or mad they bawled as loudly as yearlings. They had learned early that whining would attract some attention from their mother, even if it were a quick cuff. And after a full meal when all were satisfied the mother, as well as each cub, often rolled over to hum a happy murmur which was not very different from a kitten's pleased mewing.

Before long the black cub began an unrestrained squalling as his lonesomeness mounted. Timidity had characterized him from birth, and, although his heavier weight allowed him to bully and outwrestle Little Chestnut at times, he was considerably different in temperament from his brother.

Little Chestnut had been the evercurious and quiet explorer. The black cub was usually satisfied to follow along behind. When Little Chestnut wrestled a pine cone on a hot afternoon, however, the black cub had often curled up at the mother's back and slept.

But the black cub took the lead now in announcing his rising feeling of insecurity, and before long Little Chestnut was moved to vent his own feelings with an occasional wail himself. A hoot owl soon stopped this, however, with his own pronouncement. Although Little Chestnut had heard this call many times, now it seemed to voice a threat. The black cub shrank close to the mother bear's body.

Little Chestnut stood motionless and studied the nearby limbs. The hoot owl sounded again and the cub slowly rose to his hind feet in order to see better. He had seen the mother bear do this when searching for a suspicious noise or movement.

It was an easy feat for the bear family, for like raccoons, bears walked on the soles of the entire foot. Bear feet were as large in proportion to height as human feet, and balance could be maintained indefinitely. The owl was invisible, however.

Whippoorwills soon began exchanging calls and tonight they sounded louder than they ever had. For the first time, with no sounds from the mother to occupy him, Little Chestnut heard an endless succession of tree frogs, crickets, buzzing insects and even the sudden caterwaul of a bobcat on a distant slope as the cat tried to flush rodents into revealing locations.

The noises offered no comfort. They enhanced lonesomeness tonight, and occasionally even terror as the two cubs huddled close to each other for warmth and reassurance. Neither cub tried to sleep.

5: Strange Rites

SHORTLY BEFORE FIRST LIGHT MADE A GRAY STREAK ABOVE THE
eastern mountains Little Chestnut drifted into sleep. Exhaustion had finally overtaken alertness.

It seemed that he had hardly closed his eyes, however,
when a blue jay's squawks awakened him. The bird perched
on a swinging hickory twig a few feet away to scream angrily
at the bear family. Such irritations were to be expected from
the crested bird, however, since it conscientiously raised an
alarm whenever it spotted an animal which was a hazard to
any of the woodlands' small life. It had assistance in this
job, usually, from squirrels, catbirds, and crows, all of whom
raised indignant outcries at sight of larger, less agile, wildlife below the trees.

Little Chestnut looked at the incensed bird and ignored
it. The black cub could not dismiss the noise so easily, however, and shrank against the mother bear's body.

Fully awake now, Little Chestnut sat erect, still puzzled
as to what he should do. Although instinct guides and pro-
tects all young wildlife to a stronger degree than it does
human young, there was nothing now to suggest what he
should do. Instinct had allowed a sudden void, as if he had

encountered a canyon blocking his path and there was no way across.

Before long Little Chestnut's eyes were drawn to a clearing among the oaks across the stream. A turkey tom and his hens were standing there motionless, their heads high on rigid necks. There were no poults in sight.

The blue jay's screaming had alerted them, but shortly Little Chestnut saw their necks relax and all except one guarding hen resumed their search for the new acorns scattered among the leaves.

The turkey tom over there was the turkey patriarch of most slopes within sight, and he allowed no competing toms to encroach. Neither the dead mother bear, nor the cubs, offered a threat to his peace just now, however, so he ignored them. Although he was the holder of turkey rights on these slopes, he made little effort to dispute the other species whose territories overlapped, or included, his own. Most of the time there was no conflict, although no doubt the tom would have been pleased to see fewer white-tailed deer and squirrels sharing the acorn crop.

There were some advantages in overlapping boundaries to the old turkey, however. Each spring he temporarily extended his claim to include some of the valley barnyards where he sent domestic toms fleeing and stole their hens.

Suddenly Little Chestnut saw the tom and his hens dip necks close to the ground and race upslope, their powerful

legs taking them into the brush and out of sight faster than if they had beaten a path up through the tree limbs. He turned his eyes downslope to see what caused the fright.

He did not have long to wait for an answer. The blue jay suddenly gave a squawk and threw itself off the branch. A wooden dart careened off the swinging perch and came to a quivering halt in a chestnut log behind it. The blue jay had no time for further outcries as it flapped off through the trees.

Little Chestnut turned his head to look for the source of this strange weapon and saw a man walking along the slope toward them. He carried a pole in his hand and he was chuckling.

Little Chestnut had never been this close to a man before. The mother bear had kept the cubs well away from the highways and farms. As a result, the only men he had seen before were rangers on distant mountain trails or motorists on the valley roads.

He did not know if the man meant danger or not, but he would take no chances. He hopped off the mother bear's stiff lap and began a spiral climb up the tree. The black cub followed him and both were in their previous perches by the time the man stopped before the dead mother bear.

The man was Robert Bird, a Cherokee Indian chief. He did not have the expected trappings of a conventional Indian chief, for he wore ordinary tan work trousers, a faded blue shirt, and a straw hat. His stomach had built pleasantly outward after nearly seventy years of ample meals resulting from his bountiful crops.

He had a habit of chuckling quietly behind his white moustache when motorists stopped at his roadside fruit stand below his mountain farm, and asked him to pose with their children. He did so as often as asked since it seemed a fair exchange for obliging them to purchase baskets of apples, pears, pumpkins and jars of honey and apple juice. They invariably called him "Chief," and he encouraged it to a degree by wearing a red bandana around his neck as a movie cowboy might do.

Many such Cherokees were "Chiefs" since it was good business. They were satisfied with the arrangement, as were visiting motorists, and if any of the latter were inquisitive enough most "Chiefs" explained quite frankly that they made no claims to royal Cherokee ancestry.

Chief Bird had one ability which completely fascinated outsiders, although it had a traditional Cherokee use. He could puff a blowgun dart with greater accuracy than most men could fire a .22 caliber rifle.

The blowgun was a six-foot section of river cane, the bamboo native to eastern streambanks. Its inside had been tediously sanded as smooth as a gun's bore, and its ammunition consisted of locust-wood darts two feet long, each of which contained a soft wrapping of thistledown at its rear. This wrapping guided the dart as feathers did an arrow, and also filled the tube's bore to allow breath pressure to build behind it.

Such darts were deadly to birds and small animals, although they were of limited use against an animal as large as a bobcat. Chief Bird seldom hunted any more except for predators, but he still enjoyed plinking at targets during his walks. As a result of such long practice no Cherokee could best Chief Bird in a blowgun match. At the Cherokee festivals here on the Qualla Reservation many tried to do it, but their bull's-eyes at fifty feet looked insignificant when his darts consistently ripped the thistledown off their lucky hits in the target's center.

Chief Bird had been drawn up the mountain slope this morning by the sight of the turkey buzzards. Although there were always one or two patrolling the skies within sight almost any daylight hour, the two dozen or so wheeling overhead told of a wilderness picnic about to begin which would be far bigger than the usual dead rabbit or bird.

Little Chestnut watched his every move as he examined the bear carcass. When he had finished, the man glanced up at the cub, gave a friendly wave and turned back the way he had come.

Little Chestnut watched him until he disappeared into the mist downslope, sensing from the man's determined walk that he had something definite on his mind. His keen hearing followed the sounds of the man's footsteps long after he disappeared into the mist. Such sensitiveness of animal senses was hard for man to comprehend since many such senses were beyond a man's ability to register.

In his short life thus far Little Chestnut had grown to like this morning mist into which the man disappeared. It made a soft white sea in the valleys and made islands of ridges and mountaintops. From below the mist level it was easy enough to see hawks flying overhead, but from above it the sailing birds skirting the cliffs looked something like fish leaping from water.

A short time after the man left, the blue jay flapped back to the tree base where it gave a few more squawks. Then it lost interest in the rigid bear and Little Chestnut watched the bird disappear among the trees.

He decided it would be safe to come down when the sun was at its highest point, but he had hardly begun backing down the trunk when he heard voices and footsteps in the leaves downslope. He wasted no time in getting back to his perch. The black cub had not left his own yet, but was waiting, because of lagging courage, to see if there was danger.

Little Chestnut soon saw Chief Bird through the trees. Another man, a game warden, was at his heels. After stopping at the tree they ignored the two cubs except for one brief glance upward, and set to work skinning out the bear carcass. It was midafternoon before they finished.

After the bearskin was rolled and ready for carrying,

Little Chestnut saw the two staring up at him. Finally the old Indian shook his head at the younger man, who shouldered the rolled skin. They trudged off the way they had come.

6: Cubnappers

THE BLACK CUB FOLLOWED HIM TO THE GROUND WHEN LITTLE Chestnut backed down the trunk again an hour after the men left. The turkey buzzards, however, had waited only until the men were out of sight before they dropped off nearby tree limbs to begin their work of cleaning the bear remains away.

The mother bear's death still was not understandable to Little Chestnut, and even less so to the black cub. As he dropped to the ground beside the carcass, the huge buzzards dropped back a few feet with wings flapping threats and beaks emitting loud hisses. The sight was enough to send the two cubs retreating along the slope.

The carcass held no attraction to Little Chestnut. However, the bearskin did. He had watched the men roll up the skin and as a result, it seemed that the mother bear had merely concealed herself temporarily and gone downslope with the men.

He had no desire to approach close to the men, but if the mother bear was down there he intended to find her. His desire was nothing unusual. Although bear cubs ended their nursing by midsummer here in the Smokies, they stayed with the mother for months more, sometimes even hibernating with her during their first winter.

Little Chestnut nosed into the thickest underbrush which extended downslope in order to put the buzzards out of sight behind him. He soon found, however, that his nostrils could detect no indication of the mother bear here, and he moved back to the open woodland where the man had walked. It was relatively easy to follow the mother bear's scent here since the hide had touched twigs every few steps. Whenever Little Chestnut was uncertain as to scent he rose to his hind feet to sniff the twig ends.

The black cub followed at his heels like a shadow. So dependent had he been on the mother that he was limited in ability to make his own way now, and he meekly followed Little Chestnut without once turning aside.

The woodland gradually took on a new appearance as Little Chestnut neared the valley floor which split the Qualla Reservation. He had never been so close to these mountain farms before. Trees were smaller here since virgin timber had been cut for lumber used in the Cherokee houses and barns. He heard sounds of automobile horns on the highway winding through Soco Gap, and occasional bawls from cows waiting to be milked. The scent of evening meals cooking drifted up with the smoke from rock chimneys.

Beyond the farms Little Chestnut caught occasional glimpses of the Plott Balsams across the valley. They were a range of mountains covered with virgin "he" and "she" balsams, and stands of tulip poplar sprinkled with shagbark hickory. The angular peaks were purple in the late afternoon sky and many reached above six thousand feet to breathe the damp coolness of low-flying cumulus clouds. The names of their offspringing ridges—Yellowface, Blackrock, Thunder-struck, Firescald, Doubletop, Whiterock, and Sheepback—indicated the unique character of these mountains which tied together the Nantahala and Pisgah National Forests.

It was dusk by the time Little Chestnut reached the edge of Chief Bird's farm. Both house and barn were beyond a plowed field and highway. It took only a moment, however, for Little Chestnut to distinguish the mother bear's skin stretched to dry on the side of the barn. The flesh side was out and only a fringe of black hair showed along its edges, but Little Chestnut sensed that this was the mother bear still playing her puzzling game of hiding.

The black cub spotted the bearskin, too, and caution played no part in the action which followed. He broke into a frantic, bawling run across the field, across the road and barnyard. Little Chestnut loped along happily behind him, as eager but silent.

Chief Bird did not see them coming, although he was soon aware of them as he heard the black cub's bawls. Unfortunately, someone else saw them running across the highway. A motorist spotted them from a quarter mile down the road and let his vehicle roll to a quiet stop near the barn.

Nor did Chief Bird see the waiting motorist when he

stepped out onto his back porch to check the noise. The cubs were already before the bearskin, treading on hind feet with front claws dug firmly into this remaining vestige of the mother bear. Both noses pushed into the hair at the hide's fringes as each cub tried to assure himself that he had at last caught up with her and ended this unhappy play.

The Indian shook his head regretfully when he recognized the unfortunate situation. There was nothing to do but phone the game warden so the cubs could be picked up and released at a distant point in the Smoky Mountains National Park or one of the national forests. They should be separated from the mother's hide and this area where her scent lingered as soon as possible. He turned back into the house.

The motorist wasted no time, however. He moved instinctively, as the black cub had done. It was a primeval instinct, one which told him to seize these treasures.

Two clamoring children in the backseat encouraged the man to capture these unusual pets, and the fact that they lived in a city apartment totally unsuited to bears did not enter into his thinking. Nor did the numerous signs he had seen during the day warning against disturbing wildlife.

With a shouted instruction to his wife to open the car trunk, he climbed Chief Bird's fence, sprinted across his barnyard and seized the two surprised cubs. He had to tear them, literally, from the bearskin since their foreclaws refused to let go, and then he fled back across the yard with a struggling cub under each arm.

Chief Bird stepped onto his porch again in time to see the motorist shove the squirming cubs into his car trunk and slam the lid. Then the man jumped behind the wheel and the car roared away. Chief Bird saw more, however, as the car sped past his house. He noted the car's color, make, and such things as the poorly lashed camp gear in the cartop rack.

To Little Chestnut this rude treatment was the climax to a day of bewildering events. He began pushing around inside the black trunk in an effort to find an escape hole. There was none, however. There were several leather-covered suitcases on one side of the trunk, but there was no hole behind them.

A short while later when the car rolled into a campground Little Chestnut had temporarily resigned himself to this black cell and the brother cub had pushed against him for security.

Little Chestnut heard little talking outside as the motorist set up his tent. The trunk was not opened since the campground was filled with people who would ask questions. The luggage inside the trunk was unnecessary to the night's camp since it contained only clothes to be worn during city stopovers.

By the middle of the night when the noise outside had ended, Little Chestnut decided to make another attempt to escape. Sensing that noise would attract danger he began silent explorations. The suitcases came first.

Sharp bear claws found entrances at lower corners where the leather was wrinkled. These holes were torn larger and both cubs began a methodical search inside by pushing in forefeet as the mother bear had done at the bee's nest. Out came all manner of silken garments, expensive suits, makeup kits and bottles of fine-smelling lotions. The plastic caps on these bottles were easy to gnaw off and both cub tongues sampled the liquids trickling out onto the rumpled clothes.

The lipsticks were nearly as tasty as honey-coated bees, although not as crunchy, and Little Chestnut led his brother

in chewing apart these highly-scented morsels. Occasionally, however, the scent became too powerful, and the cubs had to wipe their noses clean on the soft clothes. Little Chestnut found that these were better than dead sticks or leaves for such purposes.

Only one side of the car trunk seemed to offer possibilities as an escape route. This was a composition board separating the trunk from the car's back seat. A few moments' clawing and gnawing worried one corner of this loose and a moment's pushing knocked it down. The seat back was shoved off its supports when the cubs pressed against it.

The approaching dawn provided sufficient illumination for exploring the car's interior. The black cub followed his brother's example of stealth, and after testing the window glass the two quietly ripped open the upholstery at every point which suggested an escape route.

The cartop came next. After stripping the overhead in a dozen places, however, Little Chestnut found metal barring the way. Dawn was rapidly taking shape when Little Chestnut began exploring the maze of wires under the instrument panel. It seemed that if he could get some of them out of the way he might get through.

This ended the attempt at stealth. One dislodged wire crossed another, and a modern, powerful set of horns suddenly trumpeted from beneath the hood, the reverberations magnified by contrast to the quiet atmosphere among the tents of sleeping people.

The car's owner was first out of his tent. He screamed as he rushed to open his car doors. They were locked, and he wore pajamas. Frantic now, he scrambled back into his tent where he shortly found his keys. After another moment he managed to steady his hand long enough to get a car door open.

The cubs nosed back into the dark trunk while the man beat on his horn button to no avail. Finally in despair, he scrambled out again to open the trunk lid as panic overwhelmed all reason.

When light flooded the trunk Little Chestnut led his brother back into the car cabin and out the opened door. With nearby tents popping open to show angry campers, Little Chestnut's immediate goal was any place of refuge. This seemed to be the dark entrance to the car owner's tent.

No sooner had the two bounded inside, however, than shrill screams proved him wrong, and with mounting fright he tore through the mosquito netting covering a low tent window to freedom.

Little Chestnut ignored the people running about him during the following wild moments. The cubs fled through them toward the wooded slope behind the campground, unmindful of overturned camp tables and dislodged tent ropes.

The campground was far below them when the horn stopped blaring. They were across the ridge crest when the motorist hastily packed his family into the shredded car to flee questioning campers. The motorist accelerated out the campground exit.

Little Chestnut did not hear the noise when the man's car ran into the game warden's truck which was just turning into the campground.

Nearly every camper heard the collision, however, and in another moment camp tables and food boxes were deserted by campers hurrying toward the accident.

No event could have delighted the chipmunks more. The campground, to the chipmunk population at least, could well have been named Paradise Valley for it furnished an unending treasure of good things to eat.

This phenomenon of suddenly-abandoned food boxes was suspicious and the chipmunks were reluctant to shed their natural wariness. There must be some hazard here which was not apparent.

Then two half-grown little chipmunks scurried from underneath the wood pile built by rangers. They stopped momentarily under a camp table to jerk pointed little heads about and make certain that the coast was clear. Without further delay, they leaped to a bench top, then onto the table.

When they popped into a box of groceries the older chipmunk population, ringing the campground like scattered spectators at a stadium, dropped their reserve and swept onto the playing field from the natural aisles through weeds and rocks.

In another moment the colorful little rodents had turned the campground into a chipmunk festival. Paper sacks and jars fell to their sides as delighted chipmunks raced from treasure to treasure.

The busy creatures filled cheek pouches and scurried back to the underbrush to their storehouses, then back to the tables to repeat the movement, again and again.

A fox terrier, tethered to an auto bumper, turned his attention from his mistress down at the accident scene when he suddenly became aware of movement around him. Shrill, excited barks sent nearby chipmunks for cover.

The alert little rodents noticed quickly that the dog offered no threat whatsoever, and most returned to the food festival. But there was time for only two more trips before returning campers saw what was happening. They began running toward their plundered tables and the chipmunks dived into the weed stalks.

As the campground was restored to order the chipmunks gathered in two's and three's on their favorite observation points, rocks and logs, to clean faces with busy forefeet and chatter like so many tired and happy children.

7: Frustrated Helper

IT WAS MIDAFTERNOON BEFORE THE TIRED GAME WARDEN STOPPED
his truck in Chief Bird's yard. While the officer told him of
the day's events they stepped to the spring house where Chief
Bird poured a glass of cold apple juice for the perspiring law
officer.

"Did your truck get more damage than what appears?"
Bird asked as he surveyed the crumpled fender on the way
back to the porch shade.

"No, not as much as I thought at first. It doesn't interfere
with driving, but it didn't help the old truck's looks."

"What did that fellow have to say?" Chief Bird wanted to
know.

"There wasn't much he could say. He ran through a stop
sign coming onto the highway. Before the dust settled,
though, he started babbling about bears tearing up his car."
The officer smacked his lips in pleasure as he finished the
dew-covered glass of juice. "I was beginning to sympathize
with him until a camper whose table he ran over on the way
out walked up to tell how the bears happened to tear up his
car. Then I realized he was the same man who had been in
your yard."

Chief Bird leaned back in a fit of chuckling while the

warden detailed the cubs' damage to the car. "That character acted as if he'd never heard of any game laws or National Park regulations until one of his kids reminded him that they had been reading warning signs all day yesterday. By the time he got through sputtering about that I finished writing him a ticket for trespassing on your property. Then he argued that you knew he was there."

This tickled the stout red man anew and he remarked, "Yes, I knew he was there, all right. I saw his backside across the field just before he jumped in his car."

The warden had one other detail. "Oh, yes. I asked him why he broke down your fence if you knew he was there."

Bird's face sobered slightly. "Well, now, I didn't know that myself. How did you know?"

"I didn't," the warden grinned, "until the man started making excuses about the barbed wire being rusty, and it was too dark to see it, and so on."

He pointed across the Indian's field toward the road. Sure enough, the top strand was broken.

"What happens now?" Chief Bird asked.

"Depends on you. He's already made settlement for taking the cubs, and he paid that camper for the table he ran over. But he's still got to make settlement for tearing up your fence and trespassing unless you want to drop the charge."

There was never any of the impassiveness usually associated with Indians on Chief Bird's face. It was constantly changing to reflect his emotions, most of which expressed some degree of mirth, or at least pleasantness. He smiled. "Well, I've got nothing against that fellow, I guess. It won't take long for me to fix the fence, and I don't think he'll sneak in again." He used his neckerchief to wipe his glistening face. "I feel kind of sorry for folks like that, who never had much of a chance to smell fresh air when they was growing up. You just as well get that ticket of mine and tear it up," he remarked as he walked out to the truck with the departing officer.

Such wisdom was a characteristic of Chief Bird. It was hard for some people to understand why the man could view things with such moderation when they affected him directly. However, he was proud of his Indian ancestry, as well as the independence and self-reliance which characterized the red man from earliest times. As passing years turned his hair white and wrinkled his face they did not erode any of this manly independence. There was no room for self-sympathy in this man whose pride matched that of any ancient Cherokee warrior.

His immediate ancestors had lived two hundred miles to the southwest near a fort—Fort Payne in northeast Alabama —which Andrew Jackson's men had set up when most Cherokees were brought together and sent to the "Indian Nation," the present state of Oklahoma. However, some of these Cherokees had land titles to their farms and remained. Chief Bird had left the Fort Payne area only after reaching middle age, and after all his relatives died. He intended to spend his remaining years near his own people, the North Carolina Cherokees who farmed Smoky Mountain valleys.

There was one significant regret from his past, however. When he was a young man a Cherokee family from North Carolina had stopped by his farm on north Alabama's Wills Creek. The man drove a car, modern for its day, and as he asked questions about former Cherokee lands and burial grounds, Robert Bird looked past his plow to the man's car.

The man's family was in it, his wife, two sons and a daughter. The daughter appeared close to his own age, and he found it hard to keep his eyes off her face. For one quick pleasurable moment he sensed that her gaze probed deep into his own eyes to identify the man behind. And he allowed himself to believe over succeeding years that she was pleased by what she saw.

He never forgot the family's name. He pictured it in his mind's eye many times. It was "East," and the name had been painted in small cream-colored letters near one of the car's door handles. Perhaps his imagination had allowed it, but he liked to believe that she had formed the word "Sally" on her fleeting smile when the car drove away.

Since he had been here in the Smokies he sometimes asked, in a studied, disinterested manner, of local Cherokees if they knew the East family. Always the answer was unrewarding, and sometimes even a joke.

"I used to know an East, but he moved out west," was one repeated answer. This would be followed by a leg-slapping laugh, and the subject was dropped. There were a dozen Sallys about his age in these mountain valleys, he was told, but none was named East.

However, thoughts about the Indian girl of so many years in the past seldom occupied him now since the possibility of meeting her again had grown so remote as to border on the impossible.

His thoughts this July afternoon were on the two cubs. Apparently they had escaped safely into the mountains. Since the campground was not many miles distant there was a fair chance that they could make their way back to this area where they were born.

Even as he speculated on this, however, he secretly wished that they might adapt themselves to a new environment quickly, and not come back. It had been a disturbing sight to see the cubs clinging to their mother's hide. Although he knew that a bear had far less mental capacity than a human being, or even a dog, it had been unnerving to see the cubs acting like lost children.

During his years here on the wooded Qualla Reservation bears had become special creatures to him. They symbolized these rugged mountains since the animals seemed a vital part of this wilderness atmosphere. Bears had formed part of the character of earliest America. They were here before the first Cherokees had come into these mountains, and they had remained here during subsequent changes. Each time Chief Bird saw a bear and cubs on the mountain slopes he guessed that he saw a scene no different than the earliest red man had seen here.

Most people laughed aloud when told that he was on talking terms with bears. He was tolerant of them since he knew it was logical enough for an outsider to assume that a man must be in less than full control of his senses if he claimed to speak with bears.

However, the ability was no great accomplishment. He had learned a few essential bear facts very early. He knew that each bear had an individual personality which characterized its actions. By simply watching the animals feed and move about he learned to identify various bears—by distinctive fur colors and patterns, the gaits they used in walking, eating habits, and by their degree of curiosity. He confirmed his distant glimpses by walking to the place where he saw them and studying their footprints. For the older bears, especially, cracked footpads made muddy tracks as distinctive to his eye as fingerprints were to a police officer.

He learned the bear sounds of fright, elation, contentment, and challenge. They were no more difficult to tell apart than similar sounds in dogs.

He found, too, that bears reacted to voice tones much in the same way as dogs. Gentle tones built confidence in most bears. Harsh tones sent some bears fleeing, and made other bears hold their ground to challenge.

Even the bears with which he had grown acquainted by frequent observation over the years reacted differently to his voice in different seasons. At mating time few boar bears would have anything to do with him. At other times these same bears allowed him to approach within a few yards.

The secret in talking to bears, he sometimes explained to serious questioners, was not what you said, but how you said it. "You've got to be real careful and polite," he would say. "Bears have sensitive feelings. They won't put up with the tomfoolery a dog has to put up with from unthinking folks."

But the really important thing in getting along with bears, he would stress, was to treat them as individuals. "They aren't made in the same mold, and they don't get the same ration of brains."

Now as he studied the drying bearskin on his barn he wondered if the two orphaned cubs had reached a point of maturity which would allow them to make their own ways. He prepared a lonesome evening meal, still contemplating his inability to lend a helping hand. He knew well the sensation of sudden detachment from his own kin. He had been very much alone now for many years.

8: Boar Country

AFTER PUTTING A QUARTER MILE OF WOODLAND BETWEEN HIMself and the campground Little Chestnut slowed. He slid to his stomach upon a cool rock and lay panting while the black cub caught up.

The flight had been more exhausting to the black cub, and he lay down several feet away to gasp fresh breaths. The black cub's pattern of existence had already been set in the short time since the mother bear's death. He was now almost entirely dependent upon the smaller chestnut cub's lead in any situation. Whatever Little Chestnut did, he would follow along as he had behind his mother.

Little Chestnut looked about him as he rested. This woodland was new to him although its trees and plants were the same as those on familiar slopes. He swelled his nostrils consciously in this invigorating mountain air to sift out scents and identify them. An occasional white cedar, or arborvitae, grew among the hemlocks below and suggested the odor of tanned cowhide which Little Chestnut had smelled when the bear family fed downwind of barns. The saddles and harnesses stored in them could be detected a mile off.

The strongest smell, however, came from the ground itself a few yards away. The leaf layer there had been overturned to expose stretches of wet black loam. Small rocks had been displaced.

Little Chestnut knew which animals had done this because he had seen them several times from a distance. They were wild boars, descended from European boars which had been in these mountains for a half century. Sportsmen had imported thirty of the animals from north Germany and placed them in a large fenced enclosure near Hooper Bald which was only a few miles away, in southwestern North Carolina close to the Tennessee border. The boars multiplied rapidly.

As hunger mounted, Little Chestnut stood and began exploring the ground for food. He was drawn to the disturbed ground the boars had made, and before long he began uncovering numerous bugs they had missed in their hurried rooting. A dip of the tongue against a fleeing bug secured it since the tongue was like flypaper.

He followed the disturbed ground until he neared a huckleberry thicket where he turned aside and sat down among the low bushes. There he stripped off berry clusters by drawing the twigs through his mouth. As he chewed these juicy berries he allowed leaves and twigs to work their way out either side of his jaws. The black cub sat down near him to mimic his action.

They had only a moment of peace, however. Other wildlife had followed the boars' plowing to search out delicacies, then turned aside into this berry thicket. A wild turkey flock was here, a fact unknown to Little Chestnut until he heard a warning "purt!"

There was no way of knowing how many rigid turkeys waited around them, but the "purt" sent hens and half-grown poults spurting in all directions, as if a house-sized boulder had rolled down to plug a mountain stream. The black cub was knocked flat by one frightened hen, and before Little Chestnut was aware of what happened the turkey tom—suspiciously like the one he had encountered before—was on his back and pecking savagely. There was no time to fight back because all of Little Chestnut's efforts were directed toward self-defense.

He shoved under the nearest huckleberry limbs, but no sooner had he emerged beyond them than the turkey was on him again, this time with spurs digging at his back. Only the thick hair and skin saved Little Chestnut from serious injury during the next few hectic yards.

Finally he managed to get enough distance between himself and his twenty-five-pound assailant to lift forefeet in defense. As Little Chestnut stood his ground the tom flapped wildly about him, the stiff outer wing feathers fanning sharply against his face and spurs cutting down in an effort to hook Little Chestnut's forefeet.

But the surprise was gone now and Little Chestnut deftly countered each thrust by the angry turkey, each successful defense seeming to incense the big bird that much more. The turkey's indignation overcame his wisdom and after a few more unsuccessful swipes the tom flapped recklessly close.

That did it. The next time spurs lashed toward his face Little Chestnut caught the turkey feet with a solid blow—sufficient to knock the bird off balance. The turkey hit the leaf layer on his side, and before he could right himself to continue the assault, Little Chestnut pounced atop him with all four feet, one hind foot shoving the squawking bird's head flat against the ground.

Little Chestnut had no particular enmity for the turkey now that he was in command of the situation, nor did he visualize the tough old gamebird as a fit meal.

The handsome tail was a temptation though. The sparkling colors of the feathers there made the rainbows in the spray of white-water rapids look pale in comparison.

Little Chestnut leaned down and grasped a mouthful of feathers from the center of this display, and the turkey jerked them free himself when he scrambled from beneath. All belligerence had been swept away with this loss, and the dethroned turkey fled in panic after his hens. Only a rain-drenched swallow's forked tail could come close to matching the turkey's now.

Little Chestnut and his brother cub spent the next quarter hour wrestling these resplendent feathers before resuming their feeding, but as the afternoon sun grew hot this activity was less attractive. Little Chestnut soon gave the black cub a

playful slap on the nose and led a game of tag downhill toward the cool shadows under the laurels.

The ground here was much disturbed and some of the older laurels stood on stilt roots because boars had rooted the dirt away and crawled underneath. Much of this shaded wallow was damp and several pools of black water had gathered in depressions.

This was a wallow of feral boars, domestic hogs which had crossed with the wild boars and now ran wild. In summer when flies or gnats were pests the boars spent hours here in comfort. The hoofed animals, such as white-tailed deer, and the elk of Virginia's southwestern mountains, used such wallows for the same purpose. Mud coated the hair and skin and encased crawling insects to hold them captive until the mud dried and fell away, or the animal submerged in a mountain stream.

The two cubs enjoyed a half hour of play in this mud. They wrestled and shoved each other with abandon and soon were well coated with the cool black mud. Only the eyes glistening in each cub's head showed that these bedraggled masses of mud were still young bears. When they tired of wrestling they settled to their haunches and splashed muddy water upon each other like children in a swimming pool.

Finally a blue jay interrupted their pleasure by settling upon a laurel limb over their heads and screaming. Sensing that this harassment might attract danger, Little Chestnut broke off the play and stared upward. The bird's outcries were not directed at the two cubs, however. It was screaming at something beyond the laurels.

Since the mud battle had lost its fascination, Little Chestnut turned toward the stream a few yards away where he could rid himself of this now unpleasant mud coat. He was distracted after a few steps, however, by a strange movement over the ground to one side.

It was a black snake, several feet long, roused from its rest by the cubs. Sensing that the snake was a fine new plaything, Little Chestnut pounced forward with front feet outstretched. He clapped his paws together on the snake's tail as the black cub loped past to join the fun.

The snake had no desire to play. Whipping about, the slender reptile feinted at Little Chestnut's face and instinct made him release the tail as he dodged aside. Then the black cub lunged at the snake's midsection, but the snake anticipated this move and feinted at him, too.

This done, the snake turned and raced off over the disturbed ground in an attempt to find some hiding spot. The boars, however, had overturned rocks and log pieces and done such a thorough job of rooting that the snake had no choice but to continue its flight with the delighted cubs in reckless pursuit.

It took only a few more yards of this for the snake to put a safe distance between itself and the cubs. Laurel limbs which forced Little Chestnut to squeeze through did not slow the snake. It was fortunate that this situation occurred.

When Little Chestnut finally shoved himself into the open again he spied the snake racing across a clearing yards ahead. The blue jay suddenly renewed its outcries, and Little Chestnut froze when he saw movement to either side of the fleeing snake.

The movement resolved into feral boars, their bulky bodies giving no clue as to their surprising speed. Two boars had the snake stretched between them before the black cub could stop alongside Little Chestnut. A third boar jumped for this prize and in another moment the snake had completely disappeared from sight among milling boars.

With his brother cub at his side Little Chestnut backed quietly into the laurels again. Once out of sight, he turned about and galloped back the way he had come.

By the time he passed the site of their mud fight Little Chestnut had forgotten about the snake, and with thoughts turned again to ridding himself of the mud, he headed toward the mountain stream which he entered at a run.

Once in the chilling current Little Chestnut ducked his head between his forefeet and curled into a ball, letting the water roll him along. After several yards of this gentle bouncing against the stream bottom he splashed ashore. The black cub had paused with feet in the water, waiting to see if the maneuver would be successful. Now he did likewise and shortly joined Little Chestnut to shake the water from his fur.

After a short climb up the opposite slope the two found a sunny expanse of broom sedge and spent the afternoon napping. It was the last such contentment Little Chestnut would experience with his brother cub. Disaster was only a short time away.

9: Place of Danger

IN ONE SENSE A CARELESS PICNICKER KILLED THE BLACK CUB.
More directly, however, it was the black cub's own father
which neither cub had ever seen before.

The male bear was with the mother bear for one week
only, in June a year ago. The black bears were polygamous
and changed mates from season to season like the white-tailed
deer. They had none of the characteristics of the monogam-
ous mountain lions and coyotes which mated for life.

Last June the male bear, with mating urges boiling within
him, had followed the mother bear's scent for half a day after
he first picked it up. He found her in a laurel grove in a
spring-fed cove. She was waiting there for no one bear in
particular, but her own instincts at this season had drawn
her there, along with nearly a dozen other bears of both sexes.

In effect, the gathering was nothing more than a get-ac-
quainted party, and the bear population for miles around
knew this wilderness drawing room. Males growled and
threatened one another and sometimes fought viciously, and
victors selected the females of their choice and headed out
along the slopes for a few days, or hours, of life together.
Each of the temporary attachments was short-lived, and the

partners were strangers again before they lost sight of each other.

In December the female bear had begun her hibernation alone, as did all adult bears except those females with un-weaned cubs. When she emerged in spring after her cubs were born, one of her primary concerns was to guard them against a possible attack by an adult male. Although a rare male could be observed playing with a stray cub, this was not characteristic behavior. A lone cub invited quick destruction if it did not climb a tree immediately whenever a male adult approached.

It was not coincidence that caused the father bear to cross the cubs' path when he did. He was drawn to the camp-ground by the well-filled garbage cans as were many bears. Some of these bears had become permanent scavengers at this campground while others visited several campgrounds on their periodic rounds.

Little Chestnut did not know the attraction of garbage cans when he saw a mother bear and four cubs in the ravine below him at dusk. They were walking directly toward the campground and Little Chestnut could not understand her disdain for human scent or noise. She had to be aware of them since both scent and noise carried for a half mile and he had no trouble detecting either.

Suspecting that she was drawn by some rich food source, Little Chestnut, with his brother at his heels, moved quietly after her, staying high on the ridge and parallel to her path.

It was nearly dark by the time he saw the bear family nose into a rhododendron bank bordering the campground. Little Chestnut was forced to move closer in order to keep them in sight and when they stopped in the bushes he did likewise.

The campground was quiet before the bear family moved again. Then they walked directly to a garbage can. The lid had not been replaced by the last campers using the can, and the she bear made little noise when she laid the container against the ground. Her cubs immediately pulled the contents out amidst the rustle of papers and tinkle of glass. Whatever they found delighted them since they ate eagerly and constantly shoved one another aside to get at other morsels.

This example was enough for the black cub. As soon as the bear family moved on he trotted forward eagerly. There was nothing left worth eating, but there was enough food smell to excite the black cub. He turned to other garbage cans and began digging into them.

Little Chestnut could smell the easily procured food but such proximity to people was unnerving. He nosed through the bushes without showing himself, and ate two half-consumed apples thrown out by children. He kept the black cub within sight most of the night, although he finally curled up in the leaves for a short sleep.

He was awakened at dawn by the black cub rattling the contents of another garbage can close to the side of a tent. Its top was off and the smell of spoiled food in it was strong.

Little Chestnut stayed in the bushes and examined a watermelon rind which some irresponsible picnicker had thrown there while the black cub pawed through the can.

The black cub's tongue soon tasted chicken salad and he gulped it with satisfaction. Few foods were as receptive to poisonous bacteria as unrefrigerated chicken salad, and during the warm afternoon and night this bacteria had multiplied significantly.

Although the tougher bear physique was not as susceptible to most diseases and toxic conditions as human bodies, there were still many which could affect the strongest bear. Food poisoning was one of these.

Little Chestnut paid little attention to the lagging black cub as he climbed back up the wooded slopes an hour after sunrise. Finally, however, the black cub's pained grunts stopped him and he turned to see the brother cub sprawled with stomach against the ground. Muscles reacting to the stresses of food poisoning were making knots on his lower sides.

The noise drew more than Little Chestnut's attention. He noticed a mother and three cubs peering over a rock ledge some distance above. Of more importance, however, was the huge male bear advancing quietly through the laurels. Squealing an alarm to his brother cub, Little Chestnut wasted no time in spiraling up a nearby poplar. By the time he reached the first limb and paused to look down he saw that the big male apparently had decided he had nothing to

fear from an angry mother. The male was loping toward the stricken cub.

It was over within the next half moment. The male lifted a forefoot and slammed it down on the cub's back the way he would have killed a hog. The black cub moved only slightly before his head fell limp against the ground.

Little Chestnut watched the male move off up the ravine. He was as unaware of any relationship with this bear as the big male was of kinship to the two cubs. The brutal scene had been without particular significance to either. To the male the cub was a competitor who had refused to scramble out of the way. And for Little Chestnut there was no attachment to the brother cub as he had felt for the mother. When he backed down the tree a short time later and headed through the woodland he paid no attention as to whether or not the harassing black cub dogged his heels.

This lack of understanding as to all that had taken place this morning also had an unfortunate effect on Little Chestnut. He had no indication that the campground had been a factor in the black cub's death. Consequently, he lost some of his instinctive wariness each night when he visited the campground. Before long he, too, was helping himself to the bountiful food supply in the garbage cans. By the end of two weeks he was arriving at the campground before dark and waiting until long after dawn before disappearing from sight.

People saw this "real-life teddy bear" with such handsome

colors and came running from all parts of the campground to watch, and gradually he grew accustomed to their stares and close approach.

Little Chestnut's handsome coloration was very nearly his undoing. Within a few days the news about the chestnut-colored cub with the white spot on his chest had traveled for miles. The information found a special reception in the ears of one man who had only recently moved to these mountains. The man had hunted bears in coastal swamps and knew some of their ways. He knew enough to sense that if he could successfully trap this unusual cub he could sell it to a roadside gift shop or service station for a price three or four times that of a black cub.

His immediate problem was to find a simple way of taking the cub without breaking a bone or otherwise marring it. As a first step he brought his hunting trailer and used it as sleeping quarters while he moved around the campground to observe the cub's habits.

Little Chestnut paid no attention to the man, even if he did look different from the other campers. His work clothes contrasted with the vacation apparel of other campers and he did not shave during the next three days as he wandered about the area.

Before the third evening he had secured the information he had come for. He knew where the chestnut cub habitually walked. Although Little Chestnut did not enter the campground during daylight, he did follow certain routes in the woods beyond, and always approached the garbage cans by the same way.

This habit of Little Chestnut's was no different from that of practically all black bears. He often followed trails which had been used by Smoky Mountain bears for decades. The trails changed slowly as the character of the woods changed and most of these bear turnpikes led to or from favored food-getting areas. Every bear in a particular vicinity used these same trails on the way to berry patches, rotting logs, fishing holes, or breezy hillsides where nuisance insects were blown away.

Consequently, Little Chestnut stepped habitually in the tracks of those bears before him, and since such bear trails were the easiest way to get from one place to another, he seldom strayed off them. Even when such trails were not easy, Little Chestnut instinctively felt some of the stubborn possessiveness of all bears about bear rights to them. Whenever a fallen tree blocked the path he, and the bears before him, went to considerable trouble to ignore it by laboriously squeezing beneath it as if it really were not there. Even large bushes growing in such paths received the same studied disdain. Instead of walking around them as a man would do, each bear pushed through low-growing limbs.

Bear trappers had used this knowledge for generations. There was no better place to put a bear trap than in a worn bear trail, or at the end of a bear log over a stream.

Consequently, it did not take this man long to spot a sapling lying across a ditch which was used regularly by the cub. Both ends of the sapling lay in thick honeysuckles and there was no likelihood of a child using the sapling as a footlog, nor would the feral boars which he glimpsed once among distant trees. A trap at either end would be effective.

10: Trapped!

THAT NIGHT THE MAN SECURED TWO LARGE TRAPS FROM HIS truck. They were not regular bear traps since the huge toothed bear traps used years ago were no longer obtainable here, but they were big enough for a cub.

The trap chains were not tied to a firm anchor since this might allow the cub to jerk free. Instead, a drag, a fireplace log, was fixed to the chain. The cub could not jerk free of such a trap and he could not drag it far. Regardless of where he dragged it the trail he left would be easy enough to follow.

Both traps were placed so that the cub would encounter one stepping onto, or off, the sapling footbridge. Satisfied that he had been able to do his work unnoticed by nearby campers, the man crawled into his truck for a few hours sleep.

Little Chestnut loved to nose through honeysuckle tangles whenever he encountered them. He liked them especially during these summer evenings when their cream-colored blossoms filled the air with a honeylike perfume.

It was ironic that the traps were placed in the honeysuckles in the attempt to snare Little Chestnut. The honeysuckles were relentless snarers themselves. They were tenacious plants which grew hardily throughout the Southeast where their tendrils explored like tongues of boa constrictors along road-banks and forest borders.

These tendrils found bushes and saplings for supports and wrapped around them. Then they drew a growing vine to the support where it spiraled up the trunk. Within a few seasons the swelling vine squeezed off the sap flow through the inner bark, and this action plus the shading effect of the honeysuckle leaves shut off nourishment and sunlight from reaching the tree. Such trees died early.

At dawn when Little Chestnut ambled along a bear trail toward the sapling footlog he had no indication that he would soon be involved in a life-or-death struggle himself. The campground was quiet. As usual there was the strong smell of people in his nostrils as he neared the log, but he had grown accustomed to this smell, and it no longer disturbed him.

He moved quietly, stepping in footsteps worn an inch deep in places. At the log he took a playful leap, as he often did, to gain its top, but its mossy surface was slick and one hind foot slipped back to the ground.

No sooner had it touched than a sharp blow hit his lower leg, and he whirled with bared teeth to defend himself. But there was no attacker. There was only the metal trap clamped tight against the leg.

A numbing shock set in immediately and by the time he was fully aware of his predicament half his leg seemed punctured with numberless thorn tips. As this sensation ebbed, an odd feeling of near-intolerable discomfort took its place.

He tested the trap's strength by trying to pull his foot free, but the trap would not remain in place. After another moment he identified the loose fire log which served as a drag.

Instinct guided Little Chestnut now as it had generations of bears before him. The laws of physics had no ordered place in his thoughts as they did in human reasoning but many of their effects were better known already to him.

Little Chestnut had learned through play and food-getting the results of leverage with a foot, of the force of a falling stone, and of the power required to pull an edible root from a rock crack. To him the trap was no more than a rock crack, but it must be fixed in place if he would jerk his foot free.

He followed the peculiar example of his kind in this situation, one which had been reported in journals by several bear trappers. Little Chestnut picked up the drag with his front feet and stood erect. Then he began to shuffle awkwardly along the trail the way he had come. The trap was a painful encumbrance each time he shifted weight to the imprisoned foot, but he moved a few inches with each step.

He soon found a maple on the stream bank which should serve his purpose and stopped to study its limbs. There was a fork in the trunk halfway to the crown. He dropped the drag log.

Grunting with pained effort, he slowly jacked himself up

the maple trunk by lifting himself with front feet and holding in place with the free rear foot. The heavy drag swung back and forth below, hitting the tree with each swing to send vibrations up the chain and into his stretched rear leg.

After several pauses for rest he reached the fork and pulled the drag log tight against it. Upon satisfying himself that the drag would not tumble free, he climbed the few feet higher which the chain allowed. Now he stopped to study the dark foilage below, to pick the most suitable spot for his jump.

There was no real choice since the area under the tree was a mass of laurel bushes. Any place was as good as another. He waited a moment more to assure himself that he would not hit intervening limbs.

Then he twisted off the trunk head first, giving himself added impetus by shoving with his free hind foot.

The pain was sharp and quick when his hind foot jerked free of the anchored trap. However, the trap's pull spoiled his leap, and he landed on his side among broken laurel limbs with breath knocked from his body.

Limping from pain and with senses clouded by his attempts to gather fresh air into his lungs, he staggered along the easiest route. This was into the campground and before he was fully aware of it, he was among tents and parked cars. Screams of delight from early-rising children summoned other campers and within moments people swarmed about the limping cub.

Little Chestnut fled between two cars parked near the stream bordering the campground. He intended turning aside once past them but he found people to either side, and he had no alternative but to rush into the water for a swim to the other side. A rough dam of loose rocks down-stream made a stretch of water nearly fifty yards across and twice that in length at this point.

No sooner had he begun swimming than he found more trouble. Children of various ages who had been exploring on both streambanks snatched up stones to splash them in front of the swimming cub and turn him back into mid-stream each time he neared the bank.

Fathers began shouting encouragement to their children and some ran for cameras to record this event. Mothers clapped in delight and hurried younger children forward. Several picked up limbs to jab at the chestnut cub's face whenever he swam close.

Swimming was no particular effort for Little Chestnut, but the jabbing sticks pinched tender lips and twice he averted losing an eye only by jerking his head aside. A number of thrown rocks struck his head.

This sport was not enough to satisfy the audience, however. Two men hurriedly lifted a canoe from their cartop and shoved out into the small pond. The current was strong for such a craft and they had a moment's delicate balancing before it was oriented into the cold current.

They began a show of their own. As Little Chestnut neared

any firm haven they held him a tantalizing few inches distant with a paddle end. Occasionally, when he turned in desperation to try to seize the paddle and use it for a moment's rest, one man would reach out bravely and place his bare hand atop the cub's head. Then he shoved the struggling cub beneath the surface.

This treatment was repeated a half dozen times before Little Chestnut had his fill of such bullying. Coughing and gasping for air, he flung his head desperately aside in an effort to get a breath.

Reacting to the crowd's encouraging shouts one canoeist leaned out holding an empty bottle someone had thrown at the cub. Little Chestnut reached for its slippery surface, but each time his paws slipped off.

His need for air grew critical. The next time the bottle was extended he reached past to grasp the man's shirt sleeve. At first the man did not seem to realize that the cub's claws really had pierced his shirtsleeve. When he did, the two-hundred-pound tormentor reacted with sudden panic. He tried to jerk free.

Little Chestnut, however, had already begun to climb up his arm. This action, coupled with the man's fright, laid the heavy man out flat onto the water's surface.

Little Chestnut scrambled up the sinking man's back into the bobbing canoe as the other man rolled out into the chilling current of his own accord. The canoe filled with water but it made no difference to Little Chestnut. He stood with hind parts submerged and front feet atop a crosspiece like an explorer about to step onto an undiscovered beach.

The canoe made shore quickly from the momentum furnished by the passengers' exits. The crowd's courage deserted as quickly as did that of the canoeists, and Little Chestnut saw only scurrying people when he bounded ashore a moment later.

This was the final indignity. The campground was no fit place for a bear cub. There was none of the fresh cleanliness of the deep woods in this place of unpredictable people. Although an ability to reason was not within Little Chestnut's capability, he knew that people were capable of almost any action. One group might offer no harm, but another could become wild predators without warning, as dangerous as mountain lions or dogs. Although bears had individual characteristics, each was dignified with a general pattern of behavior known and respected by other wildlife. But there was no way to know what human beings would do from one moment to the next.

11: Bear Country

THE MAN WHO HAD SET THE TRAPS WAS AWAKENED BY THE commotion along the stream. He was in a bad mood when he stumbled from his truck since he had not intended sleeping so late. However, the exhaustion of the previous days' long hours of searching out Little Chestnut's habits had caused him to sleep beyond his regular dawn rising.

It took him only a moment to learn that one of the traps was missing from its place by the footlog. He set out immediately to follow what seemed to be the trail left by the drag log. The cub would not be able to pull the drag far, and when he found the animal he could throw his jacket over it while he tied feet and jaws. Then he could hide the bound cub under bushes until dark after which he could leave quietly.

It was unfortunate for the man that he was not yet fully awake. The track he followed seemed to be made by a drag since it wandered in a zigzag fashion and as far as he was concerned the occasional tracks he saw were made by white-tailed deer.

The man would have done well to pause and study these tracks among the disturbed leaves. They had been made by feral boars.

The line of overturned leaves moved underneath logs where the struggling cub seemed to have made his way. The sign could not have been made by wild boars certainly, for these animals would have leaped over any logs in their paths.

The man did not notice another detail in these tracks, since right now he could not have cared less. This detail was the position of the dew claws which were imprinted where the ground was soft. The dew claws were tiny hoofs above the rear of each foot, and those on boars were in a lateral position to the two main hoofs in contrast to the deer's dew claws which were directly behind the main hoofs.

These dew claws were the remains of toes needed by the ancestors of these hoofed animals when they walked the soft mucks and bogs of prehistoric swamps. Evolution had shrunk the two rear toes as these animals moved into the firmer woodland soils over the ages, and in the case of the horse which found a home on open grasslands, evolution had fashioned a single hoof for each foot to allow for the speed necessary to outrun predators.

Because all the man's attention was absorbed with the prospect of overtaking the trapped cub he did not see the danger into which he had blundered until too late. Little Chestnut saw it, however, from the rock ledge where he lay licking his bruised foot. His attention had been first drawn to an area below him by the quiet movement under the trees. Then he saw feral hogs gathering in shaded laurels to rest after feeding.

These feral hogs—boars, sows, and piglings—were resting but alert when the overanxious man hurried into the laurels among them. They had no alternative but to consider him a threat since he did not stop or turn aside.

The man saw them only when four adult hogs rose from the shadows and lunged. Then it was too late to retreat.

He dodged the swipe of one angry sow's jaws. Another hog's tusk caught a shoe sole, however, and sliced it off as cleanly as if the work had been done by a leatherworker's knife.

The frantic man scrambled across laurel roots in an effort to climb the slender trunks, but these yielded to his weight. Before he could raise himself from danger another hog tusk tore his other shoe and his foot was bleeding when he jerked it free of the clicking tusks.

Little Chestnut watched the hogs stream from the laurels like water washing through boulders in a stream and in another moment they had disappeared up the ravine. Then he watched the man slide awkwardly to the ground and begin binding his foot with strips torn from his shirt.

Now Little Chestnut backed away from his overlook, taking care not to make sudden movements which would attract attention. Men were creatures to be avoided now. He would stay as far away from them as possible.

As Little Chestnut put the campground far below him, the clear air of these mountain slopes picked up his vitality. None of the bones in his foot had been broken, nor had the skin suffered any damage other than the loss of a few hairs. As he climbed higher the exercise gradually dissipated the stiffness which had set in when he rested on the ledge.

He spent the afternoon on an oak slope strewn with dead chestnut trunks where he ate his fill of acorns scattered among the ground leaves.

The acorns were rich, satisfying morsels and were relished by all eastern bears before hibernating. Here, too, Little Chestnut roved under chestnut leaves on virtually every slope he visited since the chestnut bushes still grew wherever blight-killed chestnut trees once abounded. As long as chestnut roots lived these bushes would continue to develop, and each year foresters hoped that the seemingly impossible would happen, that some of the bushes would develop a resistance to the blight and mature.

Little Chestnut found other pleasures besides eating among the oak trees. He liked especially the black oak family of trees since their hard barks allowed luxurious moments of back scratching. It was sheer pleasure to rear against an oak trunk and do a stationary jog while scratching to stimulate lazy circulation and rub free the shedding summer hairs. It got rid of the nuisance itching of parasites, the fleas and ticks, and allowed such a pleasant sensation to remain that Little Chestnut usually settled to all fours again with a silly grin on his face.

He soon discovered that he was not alone in preferring the rough black-oak bark for scratching. This knowledge came in an abrupt manner, one which he made certain did not repeat itself.

After stuffing himself with acorns one afternoon he felt sleepy, and upon looking around for a place to nap, he saw a black-oak sapling with its trunk split into a natural nest about twenty feet from the ground. He hitched up the trunk through a tangle of small limbs and stiff leaves which covered them.

Nosing up into the opening formed by the diverging limbs, he settled into a comfortable position. The afternoon sun warmed his face pleasantly and he fell asleep immediately.

He had no indication of the huge male bear's approach until he was awakened by the tree's violent shaking. Alarmed, he looked down but the leaves blocked a clear view of the trunk's base. After a moment more, however, he was able to see enough to know that the bear was absorbed with scratching his back.

Fortunately, the intruder had not seen Little Chestnut, but his vigorous scratching had turned the natural platform into a wildly swinging perch which threatened to split apart at the end of each sweep.

Little Chestnut wrapped forelegs around an upright limb and braced himself as best he could. Instinct soon suggested, however, that these limbs were not strong enough to withstand the momentum which his body built toward the end of each swing.

It seemed that the big bear below was pleased with the

small tree's movement, for he rocked shoulders even harder against the bark. Little Chestnut heard him grunting with apparent delight.

Fully aware of the hazard to himself if he fell within reach of this giant, Little Chestnut reached desperately with rear feet for secure claw holds on the trunk beneath. But rear claws only dug into the bark there and stripped it away.

As the sapling trembled with added violence Little Chestnut's rear claws dug into the wood fibers beneath. The result was disastrous. It weakened the trunk.

As the trunk recoiled at the end of its next pendulum movement it broke beneath Little Chestnut. Instead of flinging him free of the tree, however, enough wood fibers remained intact to arrest Little Chestnut's momentum and start him back—and down.

He came down headfirst with front legs waving before him in a frantic attempt to find solid footing. But there were no limbs strong enough to stop him, and he dropped like a rock through twigs and leaves. Before he could set himself for landing, his front paws hit a furry head and skidded down the face of the standing bear.

The bear had no warning of this strange predator which plummeted out of nowhere. He was staring absently into the distance when Little Chestnut's hard chest slammed into his forehead.

While leaves and twigs showered down, Little Chestnut became a flurry of legs and claws trying to find an anchor for his feet so he could leap free. This was not easy. The big bear's thick skin made soft footing at best and each of Little Chestnut's churning feet either pushed shut each eyelid the bear attempted to open or snagged a tender ear or nostril.

Snorting in near panic the bear flung its head about like a wet dog shaking soaked hair, and Little Chestnut was tossed into a mass of huckleberry bushes. Even before his momentum was fully arrested by this natural cushion he had gathered his feet under himself. He fled through this sanctuary and emerged fifty yards away. Behind, he heard the sounds of snapping brush above the bear's roars as the frustrated animal slapped vegetation flat in its efforts to find the impertinent attacker.

Although Little Chestnut did not see any other bears over the next few days he saw many signs where bears had fed off these oaks. Most distinctive of these signs were the "lapped" trees. Bears had made these by climbing close to tree crowns where acorns were plentiful and close to the trunk. There they settled into a fork and pulled small limbs in close enough to bite off the acorns.

This wilderness world inhabited by his own kind daily grew more satisfying to Little Chestnut. The world of human beings was far below now, out of sight and hearing. Here the air was clean and invigorating and the cool nights already had the feel of autumn. If the mother bear were still alive he would have been with her as she prepared for hibernation, and he would have hibernated with her this first winter.

Now that her death had thrust adulthood upon him, he must live the life of an adult. The next few weeks would show whether or not he would be successful.

12: Playmates and Predators

By the end of September Little Chestnut weighed over thirty pounds, six times his weight upon leaving last winter's den with his mother. By the end of the coming spring he would weigh close to one hundred.

During his lifetime of about twenty-five years he might reach a maximum weight of four hundred pounds, although eastern black bears were occasionally recorded at over six hundred pounds. None of the eastern bears seemed to have the environment which allowed the extraordinary growth of a few western black bears, one of which reached nine hundred pounds before it was taken in Arizona in 1921.

Little Chestnut's summer coat had already been replaced by the thicker winter coat and this, too, was the same rich brown color which distinguished it from other Smoky Mountain bears. The spot on his chest was as white as mountain rapids.

In many respects Little Chestnut was an adult now. It would be another two or three years before he was inclined to seek a mate, and it would take that long for him to reach an adult bear's weight. However, he could climb and move as easily as any adult, and he had not lost his desire to play, an activity which never wholly disappeared from any black bear's list of traits. Since his companionship with a brother cub had been cut short, play was among his needs. Consequently, he often went out of his way to seek a playmate, live or inanimate.

When a wind gust lifted a dry leaf from the ground he was apt to turn aside and romp after it. If he came across loose boulders on a hillside he delighted in rolling them free and watching them career recklessly downhill smashing bushes and bouncing off tree trunks until they disappeared in vegetation.

Oftentimes a stick or pine cone became a wrestling partner, and a swinging grapevine became a punching bag for boxing. Not many animals were inclined to receive kindly his invitation, however, because of his size. They were afraid of him.

When Little Chestnut heard water splashing at Lake Fontana's edge one afternoon he stopped to listen. There was also the sound of a body dragging along the ground at a rapid rate.

Puzzled by these noises he eased into the bushes and stole forward for a look. The sounds came from below a high bank before him and, with the wind in his face, he quietly moved to an observation point.

Then he saw them, three otters playing on a mud slide. He watched them with increasing interest as they romped up the bank, tucked legs alongside their soaked bodies and slid down the curving ramp on their chests. Each hit the lake surface with a splash, its effect increased by purposely awkward entrances into the water. Each otter then swam underwater a few feet to one side to a rock pile where it emerged and bounded back up to await its turn.

Little Chestnut could hardly restrain himself as he watched this happy play. Sliding, or tumbling, downhill was as much a bear's game as an otter's. He would join this romp.

He galloped from the bushes and came to a stop behind one waiting otter. Upon glancing around the surprised animal threw itself aside with a frightened squeal and flew down the slope to overtake a companion in the process of sliding. Both otters hit the water together. The third had started up, but saw the bear cub and stopped at the water's edge.

Little Chestnut promptly settled to his stomach with front feet stretched before him and hind feet trailing. He did not move, however. The slide was too narrow for the dry-haired cub.

He shoved with his hind feet. He got nowhere. Three inquisitive otter heads stuck up from the water surface to watch this strange behavior.

Finally Little Chestnut decided to do it his own way. Tucking legs and nose into his stomach he became a ball which careened down the slide to hit the water with a resounding splash. The otters dived for deeper water.

This activity was the pleasure it appeared to be, Little Chestnut found. Wading back to the bank he lifted himself

free and climbed to the top. With enthusiasm still high he rolled into a ball and repeated the play.

This time when he climbed out, two otters followed him a few feet away. When he started rolling they fell in line and splashed behind him. All three followed him to the top the next time, and by the end of five minutes Little Chestnut was just a big awkward otter as far as the three water-loving animals were concerned.

He took his turn at the top of the slide and soon the otters vied with one another in following behind the rolling cub. After they hit the water the otters delighted in circling the water-logged little bear.

After a half hour of this the play lost some of its attraction. Little Chestnut was tired and he soon paused at the top to rest while the otters continued their play. They could not understand his stopping, however, and as each passed him it managed to patter over his stomach, or at least flip a soaked otter tail against his face. Little Chestnut retaliated with playful slaps at their hind quarters.

Finally the otters slowed their play also, and as the afternoon sun warmed the slope Little Chestnut slid to his stomach and stretched his face between his forelegs. Shortly the otters settled to the ground near him to take turns napping and watching.

Such alertness was essential to all wildlife subject to attack by predatory animals or hunters. It was a necessary part of the everyday existence of bird, animal, or insect. Sometimes, however, the action of predators was so sudden or unsuspected that even the wariest prey had no adequate defense. This was the case of strange insect-eating pitcher plants only a few yards away from the sunning cub.

Almost any small crawlers—bees, ants, moths, wasps, butterflies and grasshoppers—were apt to slide into the pitcher plant's open-topped stalks after being enticed there by a sweet nectar. Sometimes lizards and tree toads were attracted to the insects thus caught, and they, too, slid into the pitfall to be slowly absorbed by the plant.

In the water around the pitcher plants other wars among insects, fish and reptiles never ended. One insect here, the giant water bug, was a savage predator which reached a length of two inches. When it seized prey—small fish, insects, and frogs—a strong digestive juice was squirted into the victim which caused severe pain, even to a bear. Little Chestnut had been bitten near the campground twice by this formidable bug. Fortunately, the giant water bug population was preyed on by hungry wading birds, ducks and large fish.

Nearly as severe a bite could be received from the back swimmers which flipped themselves out of the water at dusk to land upright, and from this position flew away on night flights which often carried them to city lights.

Water boatmen were similar to the back swimmers in appearance, but they were as omnivorous as Little Chestnut, eating both plant and animal life. These odd creatures had to breathe air so they were forced to take along air bubbles on their underwater trips.

The dragonflies, which did their flying in the daytime, produced nymphs which ate mosquito larva in quantity. These nymphs were vicious creatures, often seizing small fish, but in turn were eaten by larger fish and birds. When the nymph developed into an adult dragonfly a favorite prey was the honeybee, and sometimes dragonflies congregated in such numbers as to destroy a bee-hive's population, a serious matter to the Smoky Mountain beekeeper.

In late afternoon when Little Chestnut stirred, he found that the restless otters had disappeared into the lakeside vegetation. He was restless himself, but the environment here did not have the attraction for him which it had for the otters. The high country was bear country.

Some mountaintops were already spotted with the reds and yellows of broad-leaved trees scattered among darker conifers. Some restless urge within him pointed his nose toward this high country. He had to find something.

13: Homecoming

INCREASING RESTLESSNESS DROVE LITTLE CHESTNUT DURING THESE early autumn days and each day's travel could be measured in miles. He liked especially to explore the highest slopes when his stomach was full and there was time to learn the secrets of dark forests covering peaks above the 6000-foot level.

The high domes were worlds to themselves like no other place on earth. Cumulus clouds drifted against their windward slopes to filter into the trees and take flight again on the leeward slopes. Some of the domes were scarred like weathered warriors. Gray streaks of dead vegetation marked the thrusts of lightning from summer storms as well as flash floods which sometimes swept down stair-step ravines. Some of these high forests had been thinned by the weight of winter ice which wrenched spruce limbs from their sockets, and every slope had its share of windfallen trees strewn in all directions.

The spruce domes were sanctuaries to wildlife. They held no attractions to people and some slopes had never felt a man's feet. Little Chestnut roved this high world with the freedom of a landowner enjoying his own possessions.

But each day's explorations moved Little Chestnut closer

to the place where he was born. The trend was imperceptible to him, even though there seemed a certain magnetism which drew him toward specific peaks, and on his way he climbed the highest slopes. Sometimes an hour's walk from 1500-feet elevation to 5000 feet equalled a change in climate and plant-life to a one-thousand-mile trip northward.

By the end of October Little Chestnut had explored all the high world between the campground and the area where he had followed the mother bear. These upper slopes were free of man's interference, but it was a sparse world of limited foodstuffs. His body was not storing the fat necessary for hibernation.

Human beings or not, it was necessary to move down into lower elevations and find the rich foods which his appetite suddenly craved. One morning he crawled from underneath a windfallen spruce to find the tree limbs around him coated with ice. Without hesitation he headed downslope toward a valley which he seemed to know.

The valley farmhouses were rimmed with fields of rich pumpkins and orchards of apple trees whose fruit was a bear treasure. His first taste of apples had come during the past few days when he happened across the broken trees of a mountain orchard abandoned decades ago. Other bears had broken the trees each autumn when the apples ripened.

The way a bear picked apples was a crime in the farmer's eyes. The heavy animals broke off limbs to get to the fruit. Sometimes the bears climbed the trunks and split even these at the forks in an effort to reach the uppermost fruit. It was an unfortunate situation, but the bears had no stepladders as did the farmers.

It was on the last day of October that Little Chestnut saw Chief Bird for the first time. He had not seen the man when he and his brother cub had been captured in the old Indian's backyard.

It was not mere coincidence that Chief Bird's apple tree happened to be the one which Little Chestnut picked this autumn morning. The highway department might well have erected a sign "bear crossing" above the Chief's farm as they marked "deer crossing" in many places since the farm bordered a natural bear turnpike across the valley. Two woodlands extended across cultivated fields from mountains to either side. These woodlands were separated only by the highway, consequently, they offered adequate cover for traveling bears.

Little Chestnut walked into Chief Bird's backyard before dawn as soon as his nostrils told him that no dogs lived here. He smelled the scents remaining on the barn side where the mother bear's skin had been stretched, and although the bearskin had been taken down weeks ago and placed before Chief Bird's fireplace, there was enough scent to stop him in his tracks.

His head lifted in the darkness and his nostrils flared slowly to sift the night air. Little Chestnut recognized the scent, but he recognized, too, that the mother bear was not here. It was

not the scent of a live animal. The mother bear was a thing of the past.

Yet this place held a special attraction for him. The scent reminded of pleasant days.

Then he saw the dark apple-tree limbs silhouetted against the sky and wasted no time climbing into it. Over the next hour as the gray streak on the eastern horizon was displaced by a pink dawn he ate apples. Juice ran freely from his lower jaw and dribbled down his chest fur to attract early morning gnats.

A screeen door slammed and Little Chestnut saw Chief Bird step into the yard. Little Chestnut tried to avoid detection by remaining motionless. This was of no value, however, for Chief Bird had already seen him through his kitchen window.

The man stood for a moment looking at him, then began a walk forward. Although he was smiling and talking softly, Little Chestnut was uncertain as to what might happen next. He did not take time to climb down, but leaped to the grass.

He was running the moment he hit the ground, and he fled uphill toward the woods without slowing, dodging past shocked corn and an assortment of farm implements, wooden barrels and assorted items which the casual-living Cherokee left where they would be handy.

Chief Bird looked at his apple tree with no particular irritation. He knew that bears had no thoughts for orchard care and this growing cub was no exception.

"I've seen you before, young one," he mused to himself as he studied the broken twigs. "There's only one chestnut cub with a white chest in these parts, and I'll bet you're still looking for that mama of yours."

When he finished examining the tree and turned toward his house a skunk walked from beneath the back porch.

"Well, good morning, mama," he said gently and leaned down to scratch her chin as she stood on hind feet. She once did such tricks with more grace, but the several years of protected life under the old Indian's porch had made her stouter than her wilderness kin. She had taken up residence here as an adult and had grown accustomed to the kindly old bachelor.

Chief Bird had never married. The impression the Cherokee girl, Sally East, had made on him as a young man had never been duplicated. Perhaps he believed he really might see her again even though he was well into his declining years. He never allowed such a longing to assert itself in his conscious thoughts, however, for such a possibility was so remote as to be next to impossible. No doubt she had married within a year or so after he had seen her. Since fully half the Cherokees left the reservations to live elsewhere there was no way of knowing where she might be now.

Chief Bird received some of the satisfactions of fatherhood by befriending wildlife families which somehow gravitated to the Bird farm as if a gossiping blue jay had spread the word that it was a fine place to live. There were flying squirrels in his attic, a gray squirrel's nest in each large tree and two groundhog (or woodchuck) dens in the upper cornfield. A dozen purple martins made permanent homes in a colony of gourd houses which he had set up on the barn roof. Half the crows for five miles knew that whenever he waved his hat they could sail down and eat corn from his hand without fear of molestation.

A mother raccoon regularly raised her young ones in the barn loft in the nest box which he had set up for her. She returned his friendship by extending her own trust, and each spring she brought her young to the back steps on sunny afternoons. There she found a comfortable nook and leaned back on her haunches like a she bear to lift mewling young ones to her chest, while others sprawled over each other to nurse at her stomach.

Chief Bird often sat near her to scratch her chin or head, and when a young one was full of milk he would set it in his own lap to smooth its hair and chuckle at the pleased churring sounds which these young ones made.

Each successive litter of raccoons learned to recognize most of his words of instruction and some grew so fond of his caressing that whenever he stopped they reached up with their fingerlike front toes to seize a finger and draw his hand back down.

These raccoons were the old Indian's special pleasure. Although he had lived alone all his adult life, the loneliness of an empty living room sometimes grew overpowering. At such times a room filled with raccoons—or "bears left out in the rain to shrink," as he jokingly described them—dispelled all such unpleasantness. The young raccoons had to learn what was in every jar and box, what might be hidden under the bedcovers, and what treasures could be found behind the knotholes along the baseboards.

This sometimes led to unexpected liveliness. One young raccoon reached into a knothole to touch the nose of an indignant chipmunk, and the squeal which erupted when the rodent bit him was enough to send a half dozen young raccoons racing to their mother from as many directions.

One Halloween night when Chief Bird enticed the raccoon family in for some handouts of hard candy, one young one climbed up on the kitchen table. In the darkness he pushed his head into an apple-butter jar, got it stuck, and in the commotion which followed turned the syrup pitcher over upon himself.

Before Chief Bird could retrieve him the young one managed to turn his fur into a matted sticky mess. Chief Bird lifted him off the table by the tail and deposited him upon a newspaper before the fireplace. Over the next half hour the mother raccoon and her remaining young ringed the bedraggled one for a licking "party," like so many children at work on a gigantic ice-cream cone. Chief Bird laughed so hard that night that his bandana was moist from wiping his eyes.

Now Chief Bird wanted very much to befriend this chestnut cub. He wanted to give the young bear some of the happy times he had shared with so much of the wildlife around him. He could guess, too, that there must be a considerable amount of retarded play in this orphaned young one, for he had heard of the unfortunate events at the campground.

He was determined to dispel the impression that all this young bear could expect from people was harassment. Now, as he entered his kitchen, he believed he knew the best way to do it, and even of finding the cub if he had not gone too far.

14: Crossed Boundary

C<small>HIEF BIRD LEFT HIS HOUSE SOON AFTER BREAKFAST WITH AN</small> odd assortment of items in his trousers pockets. Two were filled with shelled corn and one contained a jar of honeycomb pieces.

As he climbed the pasture slope behind his house he removed his hat and held it aloft, and occasionally waved it back and forth. He did not have long to wait for a result.

A crow's blaring "caw" sounded from the woodsline. Within a few moments two crows flapped toward him. By the time they settled to his arm to snatch up a few corn grains in his palm, other crows passed the good news that a picnic was underway.

Before Chief Bird got to the woodsline a dozen crows had been attracted to the waving hat which they had come to recognize as an invitation to lunch. The crows followed him into the trees by leapfrogging from one tree crown to another, and whenever he stopped to wave his hat and hold up a handful of corn, they dived to eat.

Now Chief Bird extended the time intervals between feedings so that the crows drifted out to either side and ahead, and after another ten minutes he heard what he wanted.

Two crows squawked loudly at some discovery off to the right front. He smiled and headed toward the sound.

He soon spotted their target. It was the bear cub, all right, and when Little Chestnut saw the man hurrying forward he wasted no time climbing a tree. This was what Chief Bird had hoped would happen, for now he had the cub stopped where it could receive its first lesson.

Chief Bird sat down on a rock near the tree and spread the remaining corn grains across his lap and over the rock. The crows dropped down at the lift of his hat and during the next few moments swarmed around and over him to pick up the corn. Several of the birds lingered to poke exploratory beaks into his pockets in search of more corn and he smoothed their feathers and petted them while talking in soothing tones. The suspicious Little Chestnut watched these proceedings from a limb thirty feet high.

He did not quite understand this, however. The man made no move to grab a crow or to strike any of the birds. Little Chestnut would have understood even less the old Indian's thoughts about wildlife in general.

The man was no sentimentalist. He believed wildlife should be hunted and harvested to prevent malnutrition and disease on an overcrowded range. But he also believed that animals had a few of the rights which people claimed.

His was a philosophy of live and let live. A bear had a right to be hungry, and to try to satisfy its appetite with the food at hand. If a picnicker left his lunch within reach, then it was an invitation to a bear to enjoy a midnight snack.

Although Chief Bird had the reputation of getting along with almost anyone, there were a few people for whom he had no sympathy. One of the things which bothered him about some people was their double standard when it came to wildlife. Such people were highly indignant when wild animals following natural instincts crossed the imaginary barrier between people and wildlife.

If a bobcat caught a chicken roosting in a backyard tree, or if a deer walked into an unfenced cornfield to feed, the owners protested loudly, ignoring the fact that their own lack of preventive measures had invited such wildlife incursions. Campers sometimes left food in tents and were surprised when bears smelled the food and tore the tent apart to get at it.

Because of his belief that animals had certain rights to lead unhindered lives and to be protected against harassment, he had often made unusual efforts to cultivate friends among the wild populations. He had learned the secrets of making friends with whitetails, bears, and the small animals.

Although children loved his ways with wildlife, some adults thought the old Indian's mind was deteriorating. They assumed that anyone who would handle a blacksnake as if it were a puppy must be in less than complete control of his senses.

His method was so obvious and straightforward that few people believed him when he explained how he made animal friends. "I just stay in sight," he said simply.

Such a concise explanation usually served to convince listeners that the smiling oldster was living in his own little dream world. A few, however, were curious enough to ask for details and they soon learned a wilderness secret known to few.

"A wild animal or bird is like a suspicious man," he said. "It's a little leary of things it doesn't know anything about. If a squirrel sees a man in the woods and sees that he is not carrying a gun he's got nothing to worry about. But if the man slips out of sight behind a tree or bush it knows that something's up. The squirrel takes no chances and disappears.

"But when a man takes pains to stay in sight and not give any impressions of slipping up on an animal, it doesn't take long before he's figured as a neighbor and he can walk a few steps closer every time he spots a particular animal."

"Will it work all the time?" one listener asked.

"No. Most bears act like most other bears generally, but each one has his own way of doing things, just like folks."

The questioner nodded absently. "I guess some animals are like that," he suggested.

"There are," Chief Bird agreed, as if the man had asked for more information. "Most folks would bet a hat any day that a rabbit would run from a dog. But I saw a rabbit one day that was chased by two hounds. That old rabbit had a mean streak in him and he turned all of a sudden and headed right into those dogs. The first dog was so surprised he turned tail and ran back toward me. But that other dog dived for the rabbit and knocked him down.

"He made a mistake when he did that," Chief Bird said. "The rabbit kicked up with his hind feet just as a tomcat would, and the dog got ripped open. That old buck rabbit got up and hopped off then as if he was a gamecock ruling a chicken yard." Chief Bird chuckled at the memory over the next few minutes.

"Most people wouldn't believe a story like that," the questioner remarked.

"Oh, I realize that." Chief Bird smiled. "I can't rightly blame them. I probably wouldn't either if I hadn't seen it myself and heard a couple of other hunters tell about seeing just about the same thing."

Before long the crows had satisfied themselves that the picnic was over. Most flapped off through the trees but three stopped on limbs near Little Chestnut to squawk a moment before continuing their flights. After they left, the woodland soon regained its calm.

Little Chestnut heard a new sound now. The man below was talking as he stared upward. The voice was reassuring and Little Chestnut's instinctive wariness relaxed somewhat.

Soon Chief Bird walked over to the tree base and took a

piece of honeycomb from his jar. He laid this on the ground, then ambled down the slope in the direction he had come. Occasionally he stopped and placed other honeycomb bits upon rocks.

Little Chestnut waited in the tree until the man was well out of sight before coming down. The honey smell was strong in his nostrils by the time his hind feet touched the ground and he wasted no time eating the comb.

Now he turned to the closest rock which contained another piece of honeycomb. He ate this as eagerly, and shortly was following the path of honeycomb bits downslope. He did not slow at the woodsline but pushed under the fence and into the pasture where he continued on from rock to rock. Each honey bit now was no more than a single lick, but even so it was rewarding enough.

Little Chestnut stopped at the barn corner. The man was flat on his back near his back door. A half dozen young raccoons were playing over him and using him as a wrestling mat as he gently pulled their tails or legs.

Little Chestnut watched this happy play with rising envy. He could hardly restrain himself from edging closer, and shortly did take a few steps forward before coming to rest again on his haunches.

Chief Bird glanced at him several times but seemed to take no unusual notice of his presence. Reassured by this, Little Chestnut finally did what he could to join the play at long range. He allowed his tongue to loll out one side of his mouth, and then the other, in an effort to show his sympathy for this play. However, this was not enough so he ducked his head and rolled head over heels. This got a response since he heard the old Indian laugh aloud. He repeated it and heard another laugh.

This was fine. Little Chestnut performed his rolls another half dozen times. Then he looked up to see two raccoons trotting across the yard dragging the man's wide-brimmed straw hat between them.

Chief Bird climbed to his feet and shuffled after them playfully, slapping his pants legs to make them run faster. This resulted in a tug-of-war as the raccoons attempted to move in opposite directions, and Chief Bird had to retrieve his well-punctured hat to prevent complete destruction.

Suddenly Little Chestnut's suspicion seemed to melt away and he abandoned himself to his natural instinct for play. He trotted forward a few steps. At this Chief Bird took three or four playful shuffles forward, patting the sides of his trousers to accompany his steps. Little Chestnut liked this attention. He turned away and scampered across the yard like a happy puppy until he heard the man stop. Then he stopped so suddenly that he skidded a few inches on the grass. He trotted back a few steps to invite another mock attack.

Chief Bird was pleased to oblige and he repeated his leg-slapping trot. Since Little Chestnut was nearing the barn where there was no room for play, he broke aside to gallop past the man and his run took him up the pasture slope to a wooden barrel lying on the grass. Both ends had fallen out and only two rusty iron hoops held the warped staves in place.

Little Chestnut had never before seen a bear roll inside a barrel, although zoo keepers often saw it and knew that it was instinctive play for most bears. To Little Chestnut it was no more than a cracked hollow log ready for his use as a plaything.

He nosed inside it at a trot, throwing his weight against the downhill side as he did so, and the barrel began rolling with Little Chestnut inside.

He squealed as he rolled, delighted with the new sensation of rolling in this protected container. The feeling was more rewarding than tumbling head over heels down a wooded slope. Although it was practical to control direction when he rolled into a ball for a free tumble, this was nicer still. He merely pushed his feet out either end to touch the ground and guide the rolling barrel.

The sight also delighted Chief Bird and Little Chestnut was encouraged to additional antics by the man's laughing. He dug front paws into the ground to set the barrel spinning. This had an unfortunate result, however. A single stave slipped from place.

Then all staves slipped loose and the curved boards suddenly fell in a jumble around the surprised cub as he stopped with legs sprawled from among them. One bent hoop hung from his neck.

Chief Bird allowed himself unrestrained laughter at this. He sat down on a rock outcropping as Little Chestnut pushed free of the jumble and stood for a moment as playfulness retreated before building suspicion. Although Chief Bird sat still, Little Chestnut moved up the slope to the woods. It was a slow walk, however, and Chief Bird was satisfied with his progress.

The next afternoon Little Chestnut wandered back into the yard when Chief Bird was playing with the raccoons, and when the man tossed a gumdrop near him Little Chestnut ate it.

By the end of a week Little Chestnut felt confident enough to eat from Chief Bird's hand, and when two young raccoons stood on hind legs to try pulling a licorice stick from Little Chestnut's mouth he promptly turned about and sat down on them. After he finished eating he ducked his head and rolled to his back as an invitation to play. This was soon accepted by four young raccoons and for the next half hour these wrestling partners rolled about the backyard.

Chief Bird did not try to force himself upon Little Chestnut by reaching out to grab and restrain him. He allowed the cub to make the approaches he desired. It was a success-

ful method since within a few days Little Chestnut had followed the example of the raccoons and vied for the man's
attention whenever he fed them or played.

Although Little Chestnut now visited the Bird farm almost daily, his wild instincts were not dulled in any way.
These late nights were growing cooler down here in the
valley, too. Hibernating time was fast approaching.

15: Round and Round

LITTLE CHESTNUT HAD NO INKLING THAT HE WAS TO BE THE final ingredient in completing a circle of life for Chief Bird. Always the pulses of life and new generations here and everywhere followed a circle. It was sometimes large and long, and sometimes the opposite.

Some insect circles in these mountains—from larvae through adulthood and the production of new life to death —were finished quickly. But many wildlife specimens took a surprisingly long time completing their circles of life and activity. An English sparrow sometimes took a quarter century, the bullfrog even longer, and the tedious little box turtle over a century. Most surprising of all these lifetime circles was that of the great horned owl which could live more than a century and a half.

For each form of life the circle had smaller deviations, or circles, which made up the greater lifetime circle. Hibernation was a necessary part of the yearly circle of life for bears. It was normal and expected. For human beings marriage and children made up a smaller circle of activity during lifetime circles. It, too, was normal and expected.

However, Chief Bird's circle had never fully developed. He had never found a wife even though he was already older than most grandfathers. His circle seemed destined to remain incomplete.

Throughout late November and early December Little Chestnut ate at a faster pace to build the reserve fat which would carry him through the winter. Rich nuts, such as acorns and beechnuts, were especially sought after, and the layers of fat under his skin developed substantially.

Three weeks before hibernating Little Chestnut stopped eating when instinct destroyed appetite and thus provided for an empty digestive system. His stomach shriveled from disuse until its sides touched like a deflated balloon. Only unhealthy bears, or those with broken teeth or some other physical handicap which retarded food-getting, ate until hibernation actually began.

Like skunks and occasional raccoons, the black bears did not hibernate in the real meaning of the term, but only dropped into a deep slumber which resulted in a stupor. Body temperature did not drop significantly as it did in a true hibernator such as the woodchuck. Breathing did slow, however, to four or five times a minute.

In contrast, the woodchuck went into hibernation as early as September and fell into a deep sleep. Body temperature dropped until it remained only a few degrees above the air inside the den. If the den temperature dropped far below freezing, the woodchuck awakened and stirred around to prevent freezing to death. It breathed about once every five minutes and its heart almost stopped beating.

Unlike a bear which was still fat upon emerging in spring, the woodchuck used up practically all of its stored fat by February. Then it had to find food quickly after awakening, when body processes returned to normal speed, or it would starve within hours.

Little Chestnut attempted to find a suitable hibernating place on the slopes above Chief Bird's farm. He roved continuously as winter snow deepened, but was always dissatisfied with likely hibernating sites—tree roots, drafty hollow logs, or cold rock dens.

One afternoon the week before Christmas Little Chestnut crossed the ridge separating Chief Bird's farm and an abandoned farm over which he had explored several times. Little Chestnut was soon stopped by the sight of a woman walking along a fence line below him.

She seemed to have an interest in a clump of honeysuckle vines. There was something under the foliage which held her attention for many moments and she picked up a stick to lift the vines aside to see better.

Finally she appeared to have satisfied her curiosity. She drew her shawl tighter around her head and walked back across the snow the way she had come. At the fence line she turned toward the house whose stone chimney was emitting waves of heat which distorted distant trees. Although he had passed this place several times, this was the first indication of human activity around the ancient house.

She stopped at a woodpile for an armload of fireplace fuel

before stomping the snow off her shoes and disappearing inside the house. Little Chestnut moved quietly down to the honeysuckles.

It was difficult for him to make out the lines of the ancient automobile there. The vehicle did not resemble the sleek autos which sped along the valley highways. Its tires were gone, and its fabric top had long since come apart. Rust covered much of the metal body and most of the door surfaces. One door, opened to a permanent position by vine growth, had a light spot where paint was thicker and rust had been retarded.

This light spot, formed of cream-colored letters spelling the word "East," was meaningless to Little Chestnut. However, the open space behind it where a front seat had been removed invited exploration.

He pushed through the vine tangles and into the space. It was a snug place, as strong as a hollow log, and roofed with the automobile hood which had been placed across the front seat by some forgotten mechanic. This was held firmly in place by vines.

By the time Little Chestnut had turned around in this space he was satisfied with it as a winter den. The metal was cold and hard, but this could be cushioned with leaves and sticks.

He waited until early evening before beginning his work of carrying brush. Then he broke off thick limbs of cedar and oak tips and carried these in his mouth to the car. There was a field of broom sedge beyond the fence and he spent an hour or so the following evening biting off clumps of this grass and stuffing it into the car.

Chief Bird had been puzzled by Little Chestnut's sudden disappearance. He knew each potential den site within a mile of his house, and when he checked them he found no evidence of the cub.

Then he stationed himself on the ridge nose above his house in late afternoon in the hopes of spotting the cub if he were still active. The cub had been in the habit of coming down the ravine behind his barn in early evening. Perhaps it was not too late to see him and follow him to his den.

The snow cover did a good job of revealing Little Chestnut's movement for Chief Bird saw him a quarter mile away on the abandoned farm. The old Indian knew that the farm had been empty for several years now. Perhaps the cub had even made himself a den under the farmhouse. An absentee owner—he never knew the name—had rented the farm to a succession of tenants who took no great interest in the property. They allowed the soil to erode and be drained of nutrients by too many unfertilized crops.

The best thing that had happened to the farm was its abandonment. Broom-sedge grass had moved in to clothe the fields. Scrub pine and cedar would soon follow to prepare a shaded surface for oak and hickory, and the fields would return to woodland.

It was dusk by the time Chief Bird stepped down to the honeysuckle vines. Little Chestnut was already inside his den. Chief Bird could see where he was but it was too dark by now to distinguish the old auto's outlines. Nor could he see the lettering on the rusty door.

He did notice, however, that the new occupant of the farmhouse had given it a fresh look. There was something cheerful about the house now. The front windows sparkled with fireplace reflections.

Even at this distance Chief Bird could see that the torn window curtains had been replaced. There were no piles of junk on the porch or leaning against the house.

Now that he thought about it, he remembered somebody downtown mentioning that a widow from Oklahoma had moved back to her homeplace. He did not remember her name, though. It was her former husband's name, and he had never heard it before.

It was three days later before Chief Bird decided to have another look at Little Chestnut. Two more inches of snow had fallen and he wanted to assure himself that the old car was adequate protection.

He waited until afternoon when a low overcast warmed the air before trudging across the ridge. It was easier walking by the road but he hoped to run across other wildlife friends on the way. At the honeysuckles he bent to see the cub. The snow was heavy on the vines now and made a snug roof. He smiled at the shivering cub. This was natural, he knew. The cub would probably shiver for the next two months before he was fully awake again.

As he straightened he saw the name on the ancient car. At first the word "East" made no impression on him. Then he stared in disbelief.

This was the car! His thoughts raced during the next few moments at this spur to his memory, and he did not hear the crunch of snow behind him.

Then he heard a cough. Turning, he saw the woman, her hair showing beneath her scarf like a rim of snow. She started to say something, but the words stopped before they were formed. After another moment her face relaxed and she smiled. "You are Robert Bird from Wills Valley."

The old Indian found it hard to believe that she remembered—or even knew—his name. Finally he responded. "You are Sally."

She smiled. "I had hoped you would not forget."

Over the next half hour the two chattered with the abandon of a mountain freshet, and when their feet grew cold enough to remind that this snow-covered field was not the best place to stand and talk, they reluctantly slowed.

"I was wondering," she said as she turned to go, "if you would take dinner with me Christmas?"

"I would like that," Chief Bird answered. He added after a pause, "I'm thinking that you probably could use a pumpkin before then." She nodded that she could.

Little Chestnut stirred sleepily. He stared in irritation at this nuisance noise outside, but when the voices ebbed he pushed his head back against his warm stomach and returned to his sleep.

Epilogue

THE GAP IN CHIEF BIRD'S CIRCLE WAS FILLED THAT DECEMBER afternoon. He took his pumpkin over to Sally East's house the next day, and a peck basket filled with apples the day after that. He ate Christmas dinner with her that week, and with Sally Bird each Christmas since.

Actually, it could not be said that Chief Bird's late marriage filled his circle completely since the two have no children to carry on Robert Bird's name.

And yet it seems that all the ingredients really are there, for each year's wild young ones for a half mile around manage to spend considerable time in the Bird backyard. Little Chestnut is fully grown now and although the dignity of adulthood sometimes conceals playfulness it never quite hides it.

On late summer afternoons motorists passing the Bird farm are apt to turn startled second glances toward the yard. They see a huge chestnut-colored bear with a white splotch on his chest rolling down the pasture slope like a cub. When he nears an Indian woman, whose hair is so white now it looks like the finest milkweed silk, he flops open to a stop.

She laughs and drops an apple slice or gumdrop into the huge upturned jaws and the bear gets up to circle her in an awkward shuffle which most observers claim is some kind of soft-shoe dance.

The Indian man beside her is much older now in body, too, but as young in spirit as his first days along Wills Creek. He often shuffles along behind this giant bear, slapping his pants legs to the cadence.

Sometimes a mother bear and her cubs poke noses through the woodsline sassafras to watch these antics. When the light is good and the observer's eyes are keen he can see that most of these cubs have a definite chestnut tinge.

About the Author and Illustrator

ALTHOUGH BURDETTA F. BEEBE IS A NATIVE OF OKLAHOMA'S prairies, she has a special fondness for America's eastern mountains. "There are many places in this rugged wilderness which have changed little since frontiersmen first settled them," she says. "Fortunately, they are less than a day's travel from almost any large eastern city. The prettiest portion of all is that formed by the Great Smoky Mountains, the most popular of our national parks."

Camping is a favorite weekend activity and much of *Chestnut Cub* was written at campsites in areas mentioned in the book. One camping trip had hardly begun when the briefcase containing half the first draft of *Chestnut Cub* dropped onto a busy expressway near her home in Alexandria, Virginia. By the time she and her husband could retrieve the manuscript its pages had been swirled by passing cars for a hundred yards. "The unbelievable thing about it," she said, "is that not a single page was lost, although most looked as if Little Chestnut himself had been chewing them."

She believes that one of the finest traits people can have is to retain the enthusiasm of young people for wildlife and the outdoors. "You feel better," she explained, "when you are around people who enjoy such things as a bear cub's antics, or wading a mountain stream." Although born February 4, 1920, she has not outgrown, nor does she intend to outgrow, these girlhood pleasures.

Her first book, *Run, Light Buck, Run!* was a 1962 Junior Literary Guild selection. Since then steady writing has produced *Appalachian Elk* (1962), *Coyote, Come Home* (1963), *American Lions and Cats* and *Chestnut Cub,* (1963). She has been Convention Manager for the National Food Brokers Association in Washington, D.C. since 1957.

The illustrator is her husband, James Ralph Johnson, who has written several wildlife and Civil War books. Among them are *Utah Lion, Wild Venture,* and for McKay, *Anyone Can Live Off the Land*.

His illustrations have appeared in seven books. Major Johnson studied art at Howard College in Birmingham in 1943. He then served in the Marine Corps for three years, during which time he saw active service in Iwo Jima, Japan, Korea and Lebanon. In the Korean War he served as intelligence officer, briefing pilots on survival procedures, later attending Air Force Survival Schools in Japan and England. He resigned from the Marine Corps to become a field scout executive for the Boy Scouts of America. After several years of civilian life he returned to active service, and at present is with the Marine Corps School in Quantico, Virginia.

Major and Mrs. Johnson live in Alexandria, Virginia.